Discrete Mathematics
Part II

Professor Arthur T. Benjamin

THE TEACHING COMPANY ®

PUBLISHED BY:

THE TEACHING COMPANY
4840 Westfields Boulevard, Suite 500
Chantilly, Virginia 20151-2299
1-800-TEACH-12
Fax—703-378-3819
www.teach12.com

ISBN 1-59803-574-6

Arthur T. Benjamin, Ph.D.

Professor of Mathematics, Harvey Mudd College

Arthur T. Benjamin is a Professor of Mathematics at Harvey Mudd College. He graduated from Carnegie Mellon University in 1983, where he earned a B.S. in Applied Mathematics with university honors. He received his Ph.D. in Mathematical Sciences in 1989 from Johns Hopkins University, where he was supported by a National Science Foundation graduate fellowship and a Rufus P. Isaacs fellowship. Since 1989, Professor Benjamin has been a faculty member of the Mathematics Department at Harvey Mudd College, where he has served as department chair. He has spent sabbatical visits at Caltech, Brandeis University, and the University of New South Wales in Sydney, Australia.

In 1999, Professor Benjamin received the Southern California Section of the Mathematical Association of America (MAA) Award for Distinguished College or University Teaching of Mathematics, and in 2000, he received the MAA Deborah and Franklin Tepper Haimo National Award for Distinguished College or University Teaching of Mathematics. He was named the 2006–2008 George Pólya Lecturer by the MAA.

Professor Benjamin's research interests include combinatorics, game theory, and number theory, with a special fondness for Fibonacci numbers. Many of these ideas appear in his book (coauthored with Jennifer Quinn) *Proofs That Really Count: The Art of Combinatorial Proof*, published by the MAA. In 2006, that book received the MAA's Beckenbach Book Prize. From 2004 to 2008, Professors Benjamin and Quinn served as the coeditors of *Math Horizons* magazine, published by the MAA and enjoyed by more than 20,000 readers, mostly undergraduate math students and their teachers. In 2009, the MAA published Professor Benjamin's latest book, *Biscuits of Number Theory*, coedited with Ezra Brown.

Professor Benjamin is also a professional magician. He has given more than 1000 "mathemagics" shows to audiences all over the world (from primary schools to scientific conferences), where he demonstrates and explains his calculating talents. His techniques are explained in his book *Secrets of Mental Math: The Mathemagician's Guide to Lightning Calculation and Amazing Math Tricks*. Prolific math and science writer Martin Gardner calls it "the clearest, simplest, most entertaining, and best book yet on the art of calculating in your head." An avid game player, Professor Benjamin was winner of the American Backgammon Tour in 1997.

Professor Benjamin has appeared on dozens of television and radio programs, including the *Today* show, CNN, and National Public Radio. He has been featured in *Scientific American*, *Omni*, *Discover*, *People*, *Esquire*, *The New York Times*, the *Los Angeles Times*, and *Reader's Digest*. In 2005, *Reader's Digest* called him "America's Best Math Whiz."

Acknowledgments

It is a pleasure to thank the many people who helped me with *Discrete Mathematics*. First I would like to thank the many students from Harvey Mudd College and other Claremont Colleges who have taken discrete mathematics from me over the last 20 years. I have learned a great deal teaching and working with these highly motivated students. Special thanks are due to Harvey Mudd College students Craig Burkhart, Jennifer Iglesias, Jack Newhouse, Aaron Pribadi, and Elizabeth Reiland; Pitzer College student Scott Garrabrant; and Harvey Mudd College Professor Geoff Kuenning, all of whom offered valuable comments on the first draft of this course. I was very fortunate to be able to present most of these lectures to the students and faculty at Denison University and Roanoke College. I am especially grateful to Professors Sarah Crown, Tom Wexler, Jan Minton, and Roland Minton for their expertise, input, support, and hospitality.

It has been a pleasure working with the ultraprofessional staff of The Teaching Company. Although I know there were many people working on this course behind the scenes, I would especially like to thank Zach Rhoades, Matt Costanza, John Levin, and most of all, Jay Tate.

Last, but not least, I thank my family for their patience and understanding while this course was being created. I must especially thank my wife, Deena Benjamin, who is my light, my inspiration, the love of my life, and my typesetter. This course could not have been made without you!

Arthur T. Benjamin

Table of Contents
Discrete Mathematics
Part II

Discrete Mathematics

Scope:

Discrete mathematics can be described as an advanced look at the mathematics that we learned as children. In elementary school, we learned to count, did basic arithmetic, and amused ourselves with solving puzzles, ranging from connecting the dots, to coloring, to more sophisticated creative pursuits.

So what exactly is discrete mathematics? Perhaps it is easier to first say what it is not. Most of the mathematics that we are taught in high school—from geometry through calculus—is continuous mathematics. Think of the second hand of a wristwatch or the path traveled by a ball as it is thrown in the air. These objects are typically described by real numbers and continuous functions. By contrast, discrete mathematics is concerned with processes that occur in separate chunks, such as how the seconds or minutes change on a digital watch, or the way the path of the ball would look if we took a few snapshots of its journey. The numbers used in discrete mathematics are whole numbers. Discrete mathematics is the foundation of computer science, where statements are true or false, numbers are represented with finite precision, and every piece of data is stored in a specific place.

In this course, we concentrate on 3 major fields of discrete mathematics: combinatorics, number theory, and graph theory. Combinatorics is the mathematics of counting. How many ways can we rearrange the letters of "Mississippi"? How many different lottery tickets can be printed? How many ways can we be dealt a full house in poker? Central to the answers to these questions is Pascal's triangle, whose numbers contain some amazingly beautiful patterns, which we shall explore.

Number theory, as its name suggests, is the study of the whole numbers: 0, 1, 2, 3, … . Many of their basic properties were taught to us in elementary school without any reason given. We remedy that here and present you with additional surprises. For instance, why can every number be factored into primes in exactly one way? Why do the digits of a multiple of 9 always sum to a multiple of 9? How can we tell if a number is composite, even if we do not know any of its factors? Why are the Fibonacci numbers so beautiful? Although some mathematicians used to boast that number theory would have little practical value beyond arithmetic, its applications are (if you will excuse the pun) numerous, from card shuffling, to ISBNs found in every book, to Internet security. We will see how number theory forms the basis for public key cryptography, allowing safe and convenient financial transactions over the Internet.

Graph theory allows us to explore relationships between objects in a most effective way. For example, did you know that among any 6 people, there must always be 3 mutual friends or 3 mutual strangers? Graph theory enables us to prove this just by drawing 6 dots on a piece of paper, connected with lines of red for friends and blue for strangers: No matter how the lines are colored, there must exist either an all-red triangle or an all-blue triangle. Graph theory can be used to describe networks that model everything from transportation grids to how computers communicate and store information. We will answer questions like, Using a network of roads, what is the quickest way of getting from one point to another? We will see that this question can be answered using a very efficient algorithm but that a similar-sounding problem (the traveling salesman problem) has no known efficient algorithm.

Throughout this course, we will see some beautiful patterns, leading to some amazing theorems and formulas, but you will not just have to take my word for them. Using nothing more than elementary logic (requiring nothing more sophisticated than a first course in algebra), we will be able to give complete and satisfying explanations to nearly everything presented in the course. In high school, too much of the mathematics is taught as nothing more than a collection of facts or techniques to be mastered without any understanding. In discrete mathematics (and indeed most college-level math courses), the real joy and mastery of the material comes from deep understanding.

Lecture Thirteen
Enormous Exponents and Card Shuffling

Scope:

In this lecture, we discuss many applications of modular arithmetic. We begin with the Chinese remainder theorem. We then look at public key cryptography, where it is important to be able to raise large numbers to enormous powers. At first glance, there appears to be no shortcut to doing this, but with the method of successive squaring, it can be done very efficiently. Another application of this idea is the mathematics of perfect shuffles, where a deck is cut exactly in half and the cards are interleaved perfectly.

Outline

I. The Chinese remainder theorem shows that every number between 1 and $m_1 m_2$, where m_1 and m_2 are relatively prime, creates a distinct fingerprint when viewed mod m_1 and mod m_2.

    A. Observe that 83 mod 9 = 2 and 83 mod 11 = 6. This theorem will show us that there are no other numbers between 1 and 100 with this property, and that every number between 1 and 99 has a distinct "fingerprint" mod 9 and 11. In other words, the system of congruences, $N \equiv 2 \pmod 9$ and $N \equiv 6 \pmod{11}$ has a unique solution mod 99, namely, $N \equiv 83 \pmod{99}$.

    B. The Chinese remainder theorem: If m_1 and m_2 are relatively prime, then the system of congruences $N \equiv a_1 \pmod{m_1}$, $N \equiv a_2 \pmod{m_2}$ has a unique solution mod $m_1 m_2$.

    C. Since $(m_1, m_2) = 1$, there exist x and y so that $m_1 x + m_2 y = 1$, which can be found using Euclid's algorithm.

    D. A solution to the system of congruences can be given by the "max + may" formula: $N = m_1 a_2 x + m_2 a_1 y$.

    E. Proof of the Chinese remainder theorem.

        1. Working mod m_1, $N = m_1 a_2 x + m_2 a_1 y \equiv m_2 a_1 y = a_1 m_2 y = a_1(1 - m_1 x) \equiv a_1(1) = a_1 \pmod{m_1}$.

        2. Similarly, $N \equiv a_2 \pmod{m_2}$.

3. As for uniqueness, if there were another solution, say N^*, with $N^* \equiv a_1 \pmod{m_1}$ and $N^* \equiv a_2 \pmod{m_2}$, then $N^* \equiv N \pmod{m_1}$ and $N^* \equiv N \pmod{m_2}$, so that m_1 divides $N^* - N$ and m_2 divides $N^* - N$.

4. But since m_1 and m_2 are relatively prime, $m_1 m_2$ divides $N^* - N$, and therefore $N^* \equiv N \pmod{m_1 m_2}$.

II. In a perfect shuffle, the 52 cards are cut exactly in half, then the cards are interlaced perfectly.

A. We number the cards from top to bottom, 0 to 51.

B. In an outshuffle, the cards are rearranged so that card 0 stays on top, followed by card 26, then card 1, then card 27, and so on. It is called an outshuffle because the outermost cards (0 and 51) stay on the top and bottom.

C. In an inshuffle, card 26 goes on top, then card 0, then card 27, then card 1, and so on.

D. Outshuffles have a nice mathematical description. The card at position x is sent to position $O(x) = 2x \pmod{51}$, with the exception that $O(51) = 51$.

E. It takes 8 outshuffles, but 52 inshuffles, to restore the deck.

F. Discrete magic: How do you send the top card to any position n?

1. Express n in binary and follow the instructions!

2. For example, $n = 41 = 32 + 8 + 1 = (101001)_2$ says that your sequence of shuffles should be in-out-in-out-out-in.

3. The reason that this will always work is based on a technique I call seed planting, which is used for raising big numbers to big powers.

III. A naive method of raising numbers to big powers (e.g., $3^{1,000,000}$ or 3 to a 1000-digit number) would take a million multiplications for the former and effectively forever for the latter, but a smart method for those same examples takes only a few dozen or a few hundred multiplications.

A. You can compute 6^{83} in far fewer than 83 multiplications by successive squaring.

1. First compute $6, 6^2, 6^4, 6^8, 6^{16}, 6^{32}$, and 6^{64}.

2. Then $6^{83} = 6^{64} 6^{16} 6^2 6^1$.

B. For a more streamlined approach, you can do the method of seed planting. Counting down 64, 32, 16, 8, 4, 2, 1, you successively square the number but multiply it by an extra factor of 6 at stages 16, 2, and 1. For example, $6 \to 6^2 \to 6^4 6 = 6^5 \to 6^{10} \to 6^{20} \to 6^{40} 6 = 6^{41} \to 6^{82} 6 = 6^{83}$.

C. The same calculation can be done mod m by reducing the answer mod m at each step. For example, it can be shown that $6^{83} \bmod 79 = 34$.

D. The seed planting method is a fast, all-purpose method. But sometimes we get lucky and can compute $a^n \pmod{m}$ even faster if we can find an exponent d for which $a^d \equiv 1 \pmod{m}$.

Suggested Reading:

Dudley, *Elementary Number Theory*, sec. 5.

Gross and Harris, *The Magic of Numbers*, chap. 18.

Lovász, Pelikán, and Vesztergombi, *Discrete Mathematics*, chap. 6.

Morris, *Magic Tricks, Card Shuffling*.

Scheinerman, *Mathematics: A Discrete Introduction*, sec. 37.

Questions to Consider:

1. What is the smallest number divisible by all of the numbers from 1 through 12?

2. When a marching band tries to line up in rows of 13, it has 3 musicians left over. When it tries to line up in rows of 17, it has 8 musicians left over. If the band has fewer than 100 musicians, how many musicians are in the band?

3. What would be the smallest band size that would satisfy the conditions of the previous problem and also have 1 musician left over when the band lines up in rows of size 7?

4. **a.** Suppose you had a deck of 22 cards. Show that after 6 outshuffles, the deck would be back to its original order.

   b. Find the largest number of cards for which 4 outshuffles would return the deck to its original order.

5. Show that $3^{91} \bmod 91 = 3$. As we will learn in the next lecture, if p is a prime number, then $a^p \bmod p = a$. This example illustrates that this is sometimes also true for composite exponents, since $91 = 7 \times 13$.

Lecture Thirteen—Transcript
Enormous Exponents and Card Shuffling

When you were a kid, did you have a favorite number? I did; mine was 2520—I know, I was a strange kid. Why did I like the number 2520? Because I had figured out that it was the smallest positive number that was divisible by all the numbers from 1 through 10. I figured this out by trial and error, and I didn't really know the fundamental of arithmetic at the time. In fact, I figured out it was the only number below 5000 that had that property.

In other words, I had discovered using the—well, not using modular arithmetic then—but now that we know modular arithmetic, what I discovered was that 2520 was congruent to 0 (mod 2), because 2 divides 2520, and that 2520 would be congruent to 0 (mod 3) and (mod 4, 5, 6, 7, 8, 9, and 10). I should point out, some of those congruences are redundant. If a number is divisible by 8, then it's automatically going to be divisible by 2 and 4. If a number is divisible by 9, then it's automatically going to be divisible by 3. If a number is divisible by 2 and by 5, then it's automatically going to be divisible by 10. If it's divisible by 8 and 9, then it's automatically going to be divisible by 6. The only congruences left that we really need to know is that 2,520 a multiple of 5, 7, 8, and 9, and [with] 5, 7, 8, and 9, then we know they'll have a least common multiple of $5 \times 7 \times 8 \times 9$. Because 5, 7, 8, and 9 are relatively prime, their least common multiple will be their product, which is 2520.

Here's another problem: Let's look at the number 83 (mod 9), and let's look at the number 83 (mod 11). When we look at 83 (mod 9), we see that 9 goes into it nine times with a remainder of 2, so 83 (mod 9) is 2, and 11 goes into 83 seven times with a remainder of 6. So 83 (mod 11) is 6. Our next theorem is going to show us that, in fact, there are no other numbers between 1 and 100 with this property. Moreover, every number between 1 and 99 has a distinct fingerprint mod 9 and 11. In other words, the system of congruences—if I asked you to find a number n that was congruent to 2 (mod 9) and was congruent to 6 (mod 11), then our next theorem shows that it has a unique solution mod 99—namely, n must be congruent to 83 (mod 99).

This theorem is called the Chinese remainder theorem, and I'll tell you where it gets that name from later. Here's what the theorem says: If m_1 and m_2 are relatively prime—just like 9 and 11 were—then the system of congruences, $N \equiv a_1 \pmod{m_1}$ and $N \equiv a_2 \pmod{m_2}$, has a unique solution mod $m_1 m_2$. What's cool about the Chinese remainder theorem is there is, in fact, a simple formula to find the number N. Rumor has it that it was invented by a Chinese couple named Max and May. Here's how we come up with the formula for the solution: Since m_1 and m_2 are relatively prime, then we know by Bezout's theorem that there exists x and y so that $m_1 x + m_2 y = 1$, and we can find x and y using Euclid's algorithm. Here's the formula provided by Max and May: Let N be the number (Max + May), that is, $(m_1 a_2 x) + (m_2 a_1 y)$. I started the rumor about Max and May; they don't really exist, but it makes the formula easier to remember.

Let's do an example. Let's find a number N that's congruent to 6 (mod 11) and congruent to 2 (mod 9). Our experience tells us that that number should be 83; let's see how Max and May find it. In other words, in this problem, m_1 (my first modulus) is 11, m_2 is 9, a_1 is 6, and a_2 is 2. Since 11 and 9 are relatively prime, we know that there exists numbers x and y so that $11x + 9y = 1$. Euclid finds such numbers—we can do this in our heads, because these numbers are small—but Euclid could tell us that $11 \times 5 + 9 \times -6$ (that's $55 - 54$) gives us 1. In this problem, x would equal 5 and y would equal -6. Now, N is equal to Max + May; what does that equal in this case? [The answer is:] m_1 is 11, a_2 is 2, x is 5, m_2 is 9, a_1 is 6, y is -6, so Max + May would give us $110 - 324$, and that's equal to -214. Wait! That's not 83, but remember, I only promised that we were looking at our answer mod 99. The solution is that $N \equiv -214 \pmod{99}$. If I want to make that a nice positive number, I'll add a few multiples of 99 to it: 3×99 is 297; when I add that to -214, we get 83, as desired.

Why does the Chinese remainder theorem work? Here's a quick proof: Since m_1 and m_2 are relatively prime, we know that there exists x and y so that $m_1 x + m_2 y = 1$. Using the fact that $N = $ Max + May, let's verify that when we put on our mod m_1 glasses—what do we want N to look like when we put on our mod m_1 glasses? We want it to look like a_1. We want to show that $N \equiv a_1 \pmod{m_1}$. So when I'm working mod m_1, what happens? I look at Max + May, but when I put on my mod m_1 glasses, anything that's a multiple of m_1 looks like 0. It disappears. So Max + May, we see that Max disappears, because Max is a multiple of m_1, so I'm just left with May— $m_2 \times a_1 \times y$. Now let's take May and let's write her name differently. Instead of m_2a_1y, let's write her name as a_1m_2y. Now May has turned into Amy, of course. Look at the *my* in Amy; m_2y, we see from the equation above, is equal to $1 - m_1x$. I have $a_1(1 - m_1x)$, but remember, I'm looking at this mod m_1, so that m_1x disappears, because $m_1 = 0$ (mod m_1). The m_1x disappears; I'm left with $a_1 \times 1$, which of course, is just a_1. In other words, we just showed that $N \equiv a_1$ (mod m_1).

A similar calculation shows that N is also congruent to a_2 (mod m_2), and you should do that yourself. As for uniqueness, I now want to show that the only solution to this problem is Max + May. How do I prove uniqueness? The way we usually prove uniqueness is: Assume that there's some other solution and show that the other solution has to be the same as the solution we started with. Let's say there was another solution—let's call it N^*—that was also congruent to a_1 (mod m_1) and congruent to a_2 (mod m_2), just like N. If it's just like N, that means that N^* and N are both congruent to a_1 (mod m_1), which means that they're congruent to each other mod m_1. Likewise, N^* is congruent to N (mod m_2). That means that m_1 divides their difference, $N^* - m$. And m_2 divides their difference, $N^* - N$, and since m_1 and m_2 are relatively prime and they both divide $N^* - N$, then so will their product. So $m_1 \times m_2$ divides $N^* - N$, which is to say that $N^* \equiv N$ (mod m_1m_2).

Repeating this process, we can extend the Chinese remainder theorem to more than two moduli. For instance, the Chinese remainder theorem says for several moduli, if m_1, m_2, through m_t are all relatively prime in pairs—that means if you take any two different moduli in our list, and you compare them, they will be relatively prime. Thus, if you have a system of congruences that looks like $x \equiv a_1$ (mod m_1), $x \equiv a_2$ (mod m_2), and so on, down to $x \equiv a_t$ (mod m_t), then that's going to have a unique solution mod their product, m_1m_2 through m_t.

Just like Euclid's algorithm, the Chinese remainder theorem is smart and fast. In fact, it uses Euclid's algorithm to quickly find the solution. The Chinese remainder theorem has some nice applications, and I told you I would tell you where the name Chinese remainder theorem came from. I believe—and this is the truth—it was actually developed in ancient China, and they used it as a method for counting their troops. Imagine the Chinese army has somewhere between—oh, some number of troops that might be under 1000, or they might know it's between 1000 and 2000, or something like that, but they don't know it exactly, and they don't want to count every one. It takes too long to take attendance. What they can do is the following: They can say, "Soldiers, everybody line up in rows of 7." Everybody lines up in perfect rows of 7. Then the general, overseeing the crowd, sees that there are perfect rows of 7, except at the end, there were 3 people left over.

Then the general says, "Everybody, line up in rows of 11," so a horn is tooted 11 times, everybody lines up in rows of 11 and they see the remainder from that. Then they do another one with 13. "Everyone get up in rows of 13." What they discover is [that] they have a number—[for] the total number of troops, they know its remainder when it's divided by 7, they know its remainder when it's divided by 11, they know its remainder when it's divided by 13, and therefore, by the Chinese remainder theorem, they will know its remainder when divided by 1001. If the number of troops was under 1000, you would know that number exactly. Or if you know the troops are somewhere between 1000 and 2000, you'd know that number exactly. If you're not even sure you have that good of a handle on the size of the troops, then you could have them do it into rows of 17, because that's relatively prime to 7, 11, and 13. Then you'd know your answer mod 17,017. Anyway, this was the original application of the Chinese remainder theorem.

Who else likes to be discreet? Why magicians, of course, so next, we're going to apply modular arithmetic to one of my favorite topics, card shuffling. There are several different types of shuffles out there. You may be familiar with the overhand shuffle or perhaps the riffle shuffle, and those are pretty good ways of randomizing the deck. In fact, not long ago, a couple of mathematicians, Dave Bayer and Persi Diaconis, showed that you need to do about seven of these riffle shuffles before your deck can be considered to be completely randomized. But the shuffle I want to talk about is something that magicians call the perfect shuffle or the faro shuffle. Although the shuffle appears to be random, it's not random at all, which is why it's used by magicians.

Here's what the perfect shuffle looks like: We take the deck of cards and as best as we can, we try to cut it exactly in half. To do a perfect shuffle, you have to cut it exactly in half, and then you push the cards together in such a way that the cards interlace perfectly. I almost got it. If you do this perfectly, then the cards should be perfectly interlaced. You'll see I missed it here. I've got these two cards on the top, but just about everything else, up-down, up-down, up-down, up-down, OK? There's another two that are up; I probably have some down together there. It's probably because I didn't cut the cards exactly in half. Anyway, a good magician can do these perfect shuffles consistently.

Let's explore the mathematics behind the perfect shuffle. Let's label our cards, first of all, from top to bottom. Let's call the top card position 0 and the bottom card position 51. They're in position 0, 1, all the way down to 51. The first thing you do is you cut the cards exactly in half so that one half has the cards 0 to 25, the other half has the cards 26 to 51, and then the cards are meshed together perfectly. There are two ways that you can mesh the cards perfectly, either card 0 stays on top or card 26 goes on top. If card 0 stays on top, then that's going to force card 51 to be on the bottom; that's called an outshuffle because the outermost cards stay at the outside. After you do the outshuffle, instead of the cards being in order 0 through 51, we're going to see them in order 0, then the card that used to be in position 26, then the card that used to be in position 1, then the card that used to be in position 27, and so on down. On the other hand, [with] an inshuffle, card 26 becomes the top card, followed by card 0, then 27, then 1, and so on down.

Let's analyze the outshuffle. What happens to a card at position x? Let me give you the answer and then we'll verify that it's true. I claim that the card in position x is sent to position $O(x)$ (O as in "outshuffle"), where $O(x)$ is $2x$ if x is between 0 and 25, and it's $2x - 51$ if x is between 26 and 51. The beauty of this formula is that you can simplify it because if I put on my mod 51 glasses, then we'll see that the 51 just disappears. We can say that $O(x) = 2x \pmod{51}$—unless x was in position 51 to begin with; O of 51 is still at position 51. For example, $O(2)$ is 4 because the card that was originally in position 2 is now in position 4. Check that out—0, 1, 2, 3, 4. Card 2 is in position 4. [Position] $O(14)$, that's going to be 28 ($2 \times 14 = 28$). But $O(28)$, the card in position 28, that gets sent to 56 (mod 51), which is 5. Card 28 will now be in position 5, and you can verify that. We call $O(x)$ a "permutation," or a rearrangement, of the numbers 0 through 51, and yes, this is the same word and the same usage of "permutation" that we talked about earlier in combinatorics.

Here's the first interesting result about card shuffling. I claim that if you do 8 perfect shuffles, then that restores the deck to its original position. Whatever order I have these cards in, if I do 8 perfect outshuffles—just outshuffles, now—then after those 8 outshuffles, the cards will still be in their original position. I'll give you two proofs of this theorem. [First,] we can actually represent our permutation, our outshuffle, using something called "cycle notation." Here's what we do. We follow the path of every card in the deck in a rather efficient way. For instance, card 0, after 1 outshuffle, it's still in position 0; not very interesting there. Card 1, on the other hand, after one outshuffle, gets doubled to position 2, and card 2 gets doubled to position 4, and 4 goes to 8, 8 goes to 16, 16 goes to 32, and now when I double 32, I get 64. But remember, we're doing this mod 51, so card 32 is sent to 13, 13 gets sent to 26, and 26, when we double that, we get 52, but 52 (mod 51) is 1. We're back to where we started.

On the other hand, card 3 has a different path. It goes to 6, then to 12, then to 24, 48; 48 doubled is 96, mod 51 is 45, and so on. The entire deck can be expressed in terms of these cycles. If you look at the cycles we have here, you'll notice that six of them have length 8, and one of them has length 2, and two of them have length 1. What happens to card 4 after 3 outshuffles? After 3 outshuffles, where is it going to be? Counting 3 places, it will be in position 32. How about card 32? Where will it be after 3 outshuffles? It will be in position 1. Where is card 1 going to be after 8 outshuffles? It's going to be back to where it started. In fact, everything in an 8 cycle is going to be back where it started after 8 outshuffles. That will also be true for everything in a cycle of length 1 or anything in a cycle of length 2. Any number, no matter what size cycle it's in, is going to be back to where it started after 8 outshuffles. Since the least common multiple of the numbers 1, 8, 8, 8, 8, 2, 8, and 1 is 8, everything gets back to where it started.

Another proof that we can do—I'll just say this one quickly—is we can express the outshuffle by just trying to do all those cases at once. Consider a card in position x; where will that be after 1 outshuffle? It will be in position $2x \pmod{51}$. After 2 outshuffles, it will be in position $4x \pmod{51}$ because the $2x$ gets doubled, and after 3 outshuffles, it will be in position $8x$, and then $16x$, $32x$, $64x$—oh, did I say $64x$? When I put on my mod 51 glasses, that 64 looks like a 13, so that's position $13x$. I'll double that to get $26x$. I'll double that to get 52*x*. That means after 8 shuffles, card *x* is in position 52*x*, but working mod 51, that's in position *x*. After 8 shuffles, every card is back to where it started.

With the inshuffles, life is not so neat. You can show that with an inshuffle, a card in position *x* is going to be sent to position $2x + 1$ (mod 53). Nothing gets sent to position 52 in an inshuffle, which is good, because you didn't have really a position of 52 with your deck. So *x* is sent to position $2x + 1$ (mod 53), and if you put that in your cycle notation, you get one long cycle of length 52 and then one little cycle of length 1 for the invisible card in position 52. What that means is you would have to do 52 inshuffles to restore the deck to its original order.

If we combine inshuffles with outshuffles, we get a truly amazing result. Suppose I'm a magician, and I want to send the top card, the card in position 0, into some position *n*; how do we do that? The answer is—if you know your discrete mathematics—you represent the number *n* in binary. Let's say I want to bring the top card to position 41, the 42nd card in the deck. Then I take 41 and I write it as $32 + 8 + 1$, and when I write that in base 2, in binary, that's 101001. Now, I simply follow instructions. What does that give us? That gives us inshuffle, outshuffle, inshuffle, outshuffle, outshuffle, inshuffle. You can verify it for yourself, that the card in position 0, after doing an in, out, in, out, out, in, will send you to position 41. The reason that this will always work is based on a technique that I call "seed planting," which is used for raising numbers to big powers. As we'll see in our next lecture, there are many advantages to being able to raise big numbers to big powers.

If I asked you to compute $3^{1,000,000}$ (mod 1,234,567), then how long would that take? By the obvious, naïve method, you would do $3 \times 3 \times 3 \times 3$ a million times; that would take you a million multiplications. But by the smart method that I'll show you, it would only take you about 40 multiplications, using a method that I call seed planting. Or to do another example, say I ask you to take 3 to 1000-digit number mod some 1000-digit number. By the naïve method, that would take you forever, really. The smart method would only take you a few thousand multiplications, even though your exponent was 1000 digits long.

The easiest technique to explain is something that's called "successive squaring." Let's say I want to compute the number 6^{83} in far fewer than 83 multiplications. One thing you could do is you could take the number 6 and you could square it to get 6^2, square that again to get 6^4, square that again to get 6^8, then 6^{16}, 6^{32}, 6^{64}. Since 83 can be written in terms of powers of 2 as $64 + 16 + 2 + 1$, we get that 6^{83} is just the product of $(6^{64})(6^{16})(6^2)(6^1)$, in far fewer than 83 multiplications.

For a more streamlined approach, I recommend what I call the seed-planting method. Here's how it goes. Again, we write 83 in terms of its powers of 2. I have those numbers in red. And I take the number 6 and I'm going to just keep on squaring it—square, square, square, square, square, but occasionally, I bump it. I bump it by another factor of 6 any time I'm at a red number. I start at 6, and I square it to get 6^2, I square that again to get 6^4, but since I'm at a red number, I bump it with a 6 to get 6^5. Then I square again to get 6^{10}, square again to get 6^{20}, square again to get 6^{40}, but since I'm at a red number, I bump it with a 6 to get 6^{41}. I take 6^{41}; I square that to get 6^{82}. I bump it with a 6 and that gives me 6^{83}.

By the way, notice at every step, the exponent is either doubling or it's doubling + 1, which was the same thing that happened to the top card of our deck as we were bringing it to that 42nd position. But I digress. Why does the seed planting work? If we never did any of that bumping, then what would have happened? We would have started at 6 and then we would have squared, squared, squared, squared, squared, squared, and we would have ended up at 6^{64} when we were done. But by bumping it at that red-16 level, then that little 6 that we bumped by is itself going to get squared four times and, thereby, contribute an additional 6^{16} to the final result. Likewise, the 6 that's second from the bottom is going to contribute twice, and the 6 at the very bottom contributes once, and therefore, our 6s altogether have contributed 83 times.

The seed-planting method works even when we're working mod m. For example, suppose we wish to raise 6^{83} (mod 79). We go through the same calculations, but at each step, we reduce our numbers mod 79, so the calculation would look like this. By the way, how do we actually reduce a number mod 79, like at that step where we have 7776 (mod 79)? Here's an easy way to get 34. Take 7776, divide it by 79; your calculator will show 98.430... . Subtract off the 98—get rid of the integer part—and then multiply back by 79, and that will give you the 34.

The seed-planting method is a fast, efficient, all-purpose method, but sometimes we get lucky and we can compute a^n (mod m) even faster if we can find an exponent d for which $a^d = 1$ (mod m). For example, let's do the problem 4^{3002} (mod 21). Notice that if we're working mod 21, 4^3 (which is 64) is 1 bigger than 63, and 63 is a multiple of 21. We got lucky because $4^3 = 1$ (mod 21). Therefore, 4^{3000} (which is almost what I want) is $(4^3)^{1000}$. But when I put on my mod 21 glasses, 4^3 just looks like a 1, so that's 1^{1000}, which is equal to 1 (mod 21). Therefore, 4^{3002} is going to equal $4^{3000} \times 4^2$, which will be congruent to 1×4^2, which is 16; [in] mod 21, it's still 16.

You may wonder: Is there a simple way to find a lucky exponent? As we'll see in the next lecture, the answer is often yes, and it's especially nice when the modulus is prime. Is there an easy way to determine if a big number is prime? Again, the answer is yes, and the secret involves modular arithmetic and raising numbers to large powers, just what we learned in this lecture. We'll discover this in our next lecture as we explore Fermat's theorem and prime testing.

Lecture Fourteen
Fermat's "Little" Theorem and Prime Testing

Scope:

In this lecture, we apply modular arithmetic to discover more peculiar properties of primes, leading to a practical way to test whether a number is prime without trying to factor it. We explore one of the most important theorems in number theory, due to Fermat, which says that if p is prime, then $a^p \equiv a \pmod{p}$. As a consequence of this theorem, if we are given a large number n and we find that n does not divide $2^n - 2$, then n cannot possibly be prime, even though we do not know any of the proper divisors of n. We will also prove a generalization of Fermat's theorem, due to Euler, which forms the basis of public key cryptography.

Outline

I. Pierre de Fermat (1601–1655) was one of the most important mathematicians of his time.

   A. He was employed as a lawyer, not a professional mathematician.

   B. Fermat was brilliant at discovering beautiful mathematical patterns. He usually did not prove his discoveries but would share them with other mathematicians for them to prove.

   C. His most famous unsolved problem became known as Fermat's last theorem, which says that for $n \geq 3$, it is impossible to find 3 positive integers a, b, c, such that $a^n + b^n = c^n$.

      1. Fermat actually proved this when $n = 4$, and Euler later proved it when $n = 3$.

      2. Fermat wrote his last theorem in the margins of his copy of the book *Arithemetica* by Diophantus.

      3. It took more than 350 years before a correct proof was given, by Andrew Wiles in 1995.

   D. Fermat also investigated properties of perfect numbers. A number is perfect if it is the sum of its proper divisors.

      1. For example, 6 and 28 are perfect since $6 = 1 + 2 + 3$, and $28 = 1 + 2 + 4 + 7 + 14$.

2. Euclid proved that if a number is of the form $x = 2^{n-1}(2^n - 1)$, where $2^n - 1$ is prime, then x is perfect.

3. Thus Fermat was motivated to answer the question "When is $2^n - 1$ prime?"

II. Fermat discovered his so-called little theorem while investigating perfect numbers.

  A. Fermat's little theorem: For any integer a and any prime number p, $a^p \equiv a \pmod{p}$.

  B. Before we prove Fermat's theorem, let's say a few words about logic. The theorem "If p, then q" is logically equivalent to the theorem "If not q, then not p." This is called the contrapositive theorem, and you get it for free.

  C. On the other hand, "If p, then q" is not the same as "If q, then p." That is called the converse statement and needs separate proof, if it is even true at all.

  D. We use a contrapositive version of the cancellation theorem to prove Fermat's little theorem.

III. While Fermat's theorem concerned any prime modulus, Euler's generalization extended to any composite modulus.

  A. Leonhard Euler (1707–1783) made profound contributions to all areas of mathematics, including combinatorics, number theory, and graph theory. Here, we show how Euler generalized Fermat's theorem to composite moduli.

  B. For $m \geq 1$, we let $\phi(m)$ be the number of numbers in $\{1, 2, \ldots, m\}$ that are relatively prime to m.

   1. Example: $\phi(10) = 4$ counts the numbers 1, 3, 7, 9.

   2. Example: For p prime, $\phi(p) = p - 1$ counts $1, 2, \ldots, p - 1$.

  C. Fermat's theorem says that if p is prime, then $a^p \equiv a \pmod{p}$. When $(a, p) = 1$, we can divide both sides by a to get $a^{p-1} \equiv 1 \pmod{p}$.

  D. Euler's generalized theorem: Let $(a, m) = 1$. Then $a^{\phi(m)} \equiv 1 \pmod{m}$.

   1. Proof [supplemental to the lecture]: Let $S = \{r_1, r_2, \ldots, r_t\}$ be the numbers below m that are relatively prime to m.

   2. Thus $t = \phi(m)$, by the definition of $\phi(m)$.

   3. Just like in the proof of Fermat's theorem, $aS = \{ar_1, ar_2, \ldots, ar_t\} \equiv \{r_1, r_2, \ldots, r_t\} \pmod{p}$.

4. Multiplying the elements of both sets, $a^t r_1 r_2 \cdots r_t \equiv r_1 r_2 \cdots r_t \pmod{p}$.

5. Since each r_i is relatively prime to p, the cancellation theorem gives the desired result: $a^t \equiv 1 \pmod{p}$.

IV. Fermat's theorem offers an imperfect test for compositeness.

    A. Fermat's theorem can be stated as follows: If n is prime, then $a^n \equiv a \pmod{n}$.

    B. The contrapositive of Fermat's theorem says that if a^n is not congruent to $a \pmod{n}$, then n is not prime. This is called the Fermat primality test.

    C. Alas, there are some composite numbers that fool the Fermat test. For example, $2^{341} \equiv 2 \pmod{341}$, even though $341 = 31 \times 11$ is composite.

    D. But the composite number $561 = 3 \times 11 \times 17$ is especially stubborn in that $a^{561} \equiv a \pmod{561}$ for every base a. Such numbers are called Carmichael numbers.

Suggested Reading:

Dudley, *Elementary Number Theory*, sec. 6.

Gross and Harris, *The Magic of Numbers*, chaps. 18, 20.

Lovász, Pelikán, and Vesztergombi, *Discrete Mathematics*, chap. 6.

Scheinerman, *Mathematics: A Discrete Introduction*, sec. 42.

Silverman, *A Friendly Introduction to Number Theory*, chaps. 9–11.

Questions to Consider:

1. The numbers x and y are called amicable if the proper divisors of x sum to y and the proper divisors of y sum to x. Show that 220 and 284 are amicable.

2. Suppose that $x = 2^{n-1}(2^n - 1)$, where $2^n - 1$ is a prime number p. List all the divisors of x (including x itself). Show that x is perfect by verifying that the sum of all the divisors of x is $2x$.

3. Another theorem named after Fermat (sometimes called Fermat's great theorem) says, "Let p be an odd prime. If $p \equiv 1 \pmod{4}$, then p is the sum of 2 squares." State the contrapositive of this theorem. State the converse of the theorem, and prove that it is also true.

4. Without using a calculator, determine 2^{100} mod 101. How about 2^{703} mod 101?

5. Compute the number of positive numbers below 2520 that are relatively prime to 2520. Use your answer to find an exponent e for which $11^e \equiv 11$ mod 2520.

Lecture Fourteen—Transcript
Fermat's "Little" Theorem and Prime Testing

In the last two lectures, we learned about modular arithmetic, the mathematics of remainders, and saw some applications. Prior to that, we investigated prime numbers, along with some of their properties. In this lecture, we apply modular arithmetic to discover more peculiar properties of primes, leading to a practical way to test if a number is prime without trying to factor it. This material will also be the foundation for our major application of number theory, public key cryptography, which will be the topic of our subsequent lecture. Also in this lecture, we'll meet two of the most important people in the history of number theory: Fermat from the 17th century and Euler from the 18th century.

Although Pierre de Fermat was one of the most important mathematicians of his time, he was not a professional mathematician but a lawyer. Fermat was brilliant at discovering beautiful mathematical patterns. He usually did not prove his discoveries but would share them with other mathematicians for them to prove, or he'd simply leave them as open questions for future mathematicians to ponder. His most famous unsolved problem became known as Fermat's last theorem, which goes as follows: For m greater than or equal to 3, it is impossible to find three positive integers, a, b, and c, such that $a^n + b^n = c^n$. Fermat proved the special case when n is 4, and Euler proved the special case when n is 3. Fermat wrote his last theorem in the margins of his copy of the book *Arithmetica* by Diophantus, along with the immortal words: "I have a truly marvelous proof of this proposition which this margin is too narrow to contain."

Nobody ever found his proof, and it took over 350 years before a correct proof was given, by Andrew Wiles in 1995. His proof, by the way, used very advanced math, including complex analysis and differential geometry, well beyond the scope of discrete mathematics. In this lecture, our focus will be on another theorem, I'd say a more important theorem by Fermat, which he discovered while investigating perfect numbers. A "perfect number" is a number that is equal to the sum of its proper divisors. For example, 6 is a perfect number because its proper divisors are 1, 2, and 3, and $6 = 1 + 2 + 3$. [The next perfect number is] 28; its proper divisors are 1, 2, 4, 7, 14, and when you add those numbers together, you get 28.

As you can imagine, perfect numbers are pretty rare. The first four perfect numbers are 6, 28, 496, and 8128. Do we see a pattern with those numbers? If you look at their prime factorization—always a good thing to do—you'll notice that 6 is 2×3; 28 is 4×7; 496 is 16×31; 8128 is 64×127. In all of these cases, we have a power of 2 times a number that is almost twice as big; in fact, it's 1 less than twice as big.

Euclid proved that if a number had that form, that is, if x was of the form $2^{n-1}(2^n - 1)$—I have to pause after the -1 that time—where 2^{n-1} is prime, like 3, 7, 31, 127—those are all prime numbers—then x is perfect. Now, 2000 years later, Euler proved that all even perfect numbers have that form. We still don't know if there are any odd perfect numbers, but if such numbers exist, it's been proved that they must have at least 300 digits. This led Fermat to ask the question: When is the number $2^n - 1$ prime? If he could answer that, he could discover and understand better the perfect numbers.

It can be shown that if n is composite, that $2^n - 1$ is also going to be composite. But prime exponents can also produce composite numbers. For example, 11 is prime, but $2^{11} - 1$ is 2047, and that's composite; it's 23×89. Fermat asked: For a given prime p, when does p divide the number $2^n - 1$? In other words, he fixed the number p, and he was looking for exponents n which satisfied $2^n \equiv 1 \pmod{p}$.

When is $2^n \equiv 1 \pmod{p}$? Looking at lots of examples, Fermat discovered that this congruence was always satisfied when n was equal to the number $p - 1$—it was true for other values of n, too, but it was always true when n was $p - 1$. In other words, for any odd prime p, he found out that $2^{p-1} \equiv 1 \pmod{p}$. Multiplying both sides by the number 2, you get $2^p \equiv 2 \pmod{p}$. For any prime, p, $2^p \equiv 2 \pmod{p}$. Fermat then noticed that there was nothing special about the number 2 either. He went on to claim for any integer a and any prime number p, a^p must be congruent to $a \pmod{p}$. This became known as Fermat's little theorem. But Fermat's little theorem is a very positive result. Fermat's last theorem is somewhat of a negative result. That's why I think the little theorem is more important than the last theorem.

Let's do an example. Fermat's little theorem says: Take the prime 11; then Fermat will predict that 2^{11} will be congruent to 2 (mod 11). Now 2^{11} is 2048; we know how to reduce numbers mod 11, and that happens to give us 2, just like Fermat predicts. How about $3^{11} \pmod{11}$? Fermat predicts the answer of 3, and if you take 3^{11} and reduce it mod 11—like we know how to do—we get 3. Fermat didn't have the notation of modular arithmetic in his day; that was invented by Gauss much later. He stated in a letter that he wrote in 1640: If p is prime, then p divides the difference; p divides $a^p - a$. This was eventually proved by Leibniz in 1683 and independently by Euler in 1736.

Before we prove Fermat's theorem, we should say a few words about logic. Let's take the statement "If p, then q." Logically, that is equivalent to the statement "If not q, then not p." This is called the "contrapositive statement," and you get it for free. For example, let's suppose you accept the statement "If it's Monday, then we're tired." That's equivalent to the statement "If we're not tired, then it's not Monday." Those statements have the same content. Let's give a mathematical example. The statement "If n is a multiple of 16, then n is even" is equivalent to the contrapositive statement "If n is odd, then n is not a multiple of 16." On the other hand, the statement "If p, then q" is not the same as the statement "If q, then p." That's called the "converse statement," and that needs a separate proof all its own, if it's even true at all. For example, the statement "If it's Monday, then we're tired" is not the same as the statement "If we're tired, then it's Monday."

Let's recall from our first lecture on modular arithmetic the cancellation theorem; we're going to use this in our proof of Fermat's little theorem. The cancellation theorem says this: Given any two relatively prime numbers a and m, if $ax \equiv ay \pmod{m}$, then we can cancel the a's from both sides to get $x \equiv y \pmod{m}$. Since we have a true statement, a true theorem, let's look at what we get for free. The contrapositive statement says: For any relatively prime numbers a and m, if x is not congruent to $y \pmod{m}$, then ax is not congruent to $ay \pmod{m}$. That's the contrapositive of the last theorem. We'll use this version, the contrapositive version of the cancellation theorem, in our proof of Fermat's little theorem.

By the way, before I prove Fermat's little theorem, it's OK if you don't completely follow this proof. It's more important to remember what the theorem says. If I lose you, that's OK this time. Here's Fermat's theorem. It says: Let a be any number. If p is prime, then $a^p \equiv a \pmod{p}$. Here's the proof. Since p is prime, it has two positive divisors, p and 1. Therefore, if I ask for the greatest common divisor of a and p, the only possible answers we could get are p or 1. If the greatest common divisor is p, then life is very easy. That means that p divides a, and therefore, $a \equiv 0 \pmod{p}$. So by the power theorem, I can raise both sides to the pth power to get $a^p \equiv 0^p$, which of course, equals 0, and $0 \equiv a \pmod{p}$. Therefore, $a^p \equiv a \pmod{p}$. We're done with the proof in the case where a and p have a greatest common divisor of p.

Suppose that a and p have a greatest common divisor of 1; that is, assume that a and p are relatively prime. Consider all the numbers 1 through $p - 1$. What do we know about those numbers? First of all, we know that they're all relatively prime to p because p is prime, and we also know that they're all different mod p. None of them differs by a multiple of p; there just isn't room. If we multiply each of these numbers by a—and remember, a is relatively prime to p—then our new version of the cancellation theorem, the contrapositive, says that since the numbers 1 through $p - 1$ are all different mod p, then the numbers $1a$, $2a$, $3a$, up through $p - 1a$ are all different mod p.

When I put on my mod p glasses and I look at those numbers, everything looks like a number between 0 and $p - 1$. But can any of those numbers be 0 $\pmod{p}$? That is, can any of them be multiples of p? No, since p is prime and a is relatively prime to p. Therefore, these $p - 1$ numbers, $1a$, $2a$, $3a$, up through $p - 1a$, must all be congruent to the numbers 1 through $p - 1$, in some order, because we know that all of those numbers are different mod p, and none of them are 0 mod p, so they have to be the numbers 1 through $p - 1$ when you look at them mod p.

Now, I'm going to multiply all those numbers together mod p—$1a$, $2a$, $3a$, all the way up through $p - 1a$—I'm just going to collapse them together. And what do we get? Well, $(1a)(2a)(3a)$ up to $p - 1a$, when I put on my mod p glasses, that's equal to $1 \times 2 \times 3$ up through $p - 1 \pmod{p}$. The right-hand side, that's $(p -)1! \pmod{p}$. The left side is also $(p - 1)!$, but every one of those terms has an a in it, so I can pull that a out and get an a^{p-1} term. Can I cancel that $(p - 1)!$ from both sides? Yes, because $(p - 1)!$ is relatively prime to p. Again, I'm using the fact that p is a prime number here, so all the numbers 1 through $p - 1$ are relatively prime to it. When I cancel that $(p - 1)!$ from both sides, we get $a^{p-1} \equiv 1 \pmod{p}$. Finally, I take that congruence, multiply both sides by a, and that tells me that

$a^p \equiv a \pmod{p}$, which is what we want. We'll have more to say about Fermat's theorem later in this lecture, but now let's bring Euler into the picture. Leonhard Euler is certainly one of the greatest mathematicians of all time—up there with Euclid, Archimedes, Newton, and Gauss—who made profound contributions to all areas of mathematics, including combinatorics, number theory, and graph theory—the discrete mathematical topics of this lecture series.

Fermat's theorem says: If p is prime, then $a^p \equiv a \pmod{p}$. When a and p are relatively prime, then we can use the cancellation theorem to divide both sides by a to get the congruence $a^{p-1} \equiv 1 \pmod{p}$. Euler wondered what you can say when the modulus is composite, because Fermat's theorem requires the modulus to be prime. He wondered what can we say when the modulus is composite? To do this, he invented the ϕ function, which has nothing to do with Fibonacci numbers. Here's what Euler's ϕ function is: For m greater than or equal to 1, $\phi(m)$ is defined to be the number of numbers in the set 1 through m that are relatively prime to m. For example, when m is 10, I look at all the numbers in the set 1 through 10, and I count how many of those are relatively prime to 10. Here, the relatively prime numbers are 1, 3, 7, and 9; therefore, $\phi(10) = 4$.

Here's another example: If m is equal to p, a prime number, then I'm looking at the set of numbers 1 through p, how many of those numbers are relatively prime to p? Almost all of them; p is not relatively prime to p, but all the other numbers—because p is prime—1 through $p - 1$ are relatively prime to p; therefore, $\phi(p)$ would be $p - 1$. Fermat's theorem says: If p is prime and if a is relatively prime to p, then $a^{p-1} \equiv 1 \pmod{p}$. Euler generalized this as follows: Let m be any number; let it be composite, that's fine. Composite or prime, I don't care, just let a and m be relatively prime, and then $a^{\phi(m)} \equiv 1 \pmod{m}$. Notice that when $m = p$, a prime number, then since $\phi(p)$ is $p - 1$, this gives us Fermat's little theorem, right? It would just say that a^{p-1}, which is $a^{\phi(p)}$, would be congruent to 1 $\pmod{p}$.

Let's do a numerical example of Euler's theorem. Suppose a is 7 and m is 10, then we know that $\phi(10) = 4$. So $a^{\phi(m)}$ would be 7^4. That equals 2401. When you look at that mod 10, you get 1, just as Euler predicts. This may not seem like a very profound theorem, but when I teach this class at Harvey Mudd College, I try to convince them of its importance by making an analogy with physics. They've all had physics in high school, and I asked them: What was the most important formula in high school physics? Almost in unison they say, $F = ma$ (force equals mass times acceleration). Well, look at Euler's theorem. You've got the m, you've got the a, and you even have the Greek letter for F [ϕ], so you know it has to be important. Anyway, the proof of Euler's theorem is practically the same as the proof of Fermat's theorem, and I won't present it here, although it is in the course guidebook. The main difference is that while Fermat's theorem deals with modulo of prime, Euler's theorem works modulo m, where m could be prime or composite.

Let's find a formula for $\phi(m)$. There's a simple formula based on the prime factorization of m. Here's what it says: If m has prime factors—p_1, p_2, up through p_k—then $\phi(m) = m(1 - 1/p_1)(1 - 1/p_2)$, all the way up to $(1 - 1/p_k)$. For example, if m is 504, 504 has a prime factorization of $2^3 \times 3^2 \times 7^1$, but the only prime factors are 2, 3, and 7. So $\phi(504)$ is $504(1 - 1/2)(1 - 1/3)(1 - 1/7)$. That makes a certain intuitive amount of sense because, if you think about it, with $\phi(504)$, we look at all the numbers from 1 to 504, and we want to get rid of those that have a common factor with 504. In other words, we want to get rid of everything that's a multiple of 2, a multiple of 3, or a multiple of 7. That $1 - 1/2$, what it does is it gets rid of all the odd numbers, because half of the numbers are odd, half of the numbers are even. Then when you multiply it by $1 - 1/3$, it's getting rid of those remaining numbers that are multiples of 3. Then, the $1 - 1/7$ is getting rid of those numbers that are multiples of 7. That's the intuition behind it.

A rigorous proof would use the principle of inclusion-exclusion, like we did in Lecture Six. Here's a quick proof by the principle of inclusion-exclusion. Starting with the numbers from 1 to 504, we first get rid of the multiples of 2, the multiples of 3, and the multiples of 7. Literally, we've subtracted 504/2 numbers − 504/3 numbers − 504/7 numbers. But we've subtracted too much. We have to add back those numbers that are multiples of 2 and 3—that's the next term—plus multiples of 2 and 7, plus multiples 3 and 7, but we've added back too much. We have to subtract off those numbers that are multiples of 2, 3, and 7, and since 2, 3, and 7 are relatively prime, there are $504/2 \times 3 \times 7$ of them. The rest is just algebra, giving you a proof of why $\phi(504)$ should have its form. The same proof strategy will work for any number regardless of how many prime factors it has.

When we do public key cryptography, we need this special case: Suppose p and q are different prime numbers, and let m be equal to the product pq. Then, $\phi(pq)$, by the formula we just learned, is $pq(1 - 1/p)(1 - 1/q)$, and $p(1 - 1/p)$ is $p - 1$, and $q(1 - 1/q)$ is $q - 1$. Therefore, $\phi(pq) = (p - 1)(q - 1)$. But look here, since p and q are prime, $p - 1$ is the same as $\phi(p)$, and $q - 1$ is the same as $\phi(q)$. Therefore, we've shown that when p and q are prime, $\phi(pq) = \phi(p)\phi(q)$. Is that relationship true for any two numbers? Unfortunately, [it's] not. Let's take a simple example: 4 is 2×2, but $\phi(4)$ is not equal to $\phi(2)\phi(2)$. However, it is true when x and y are relatively prime. I won't give the proof, but it's a corollary worth knowing. If x and y are relatively prime, then $\phi(xy)$ is equal to $\phi(x)\phi(y)$.

Let's turn our attention now to some applications of Euler's theorem. In our lecture on the pigeonhole principle, we proved that there was some power of 3 that ends in 001. In other words, there's some integer n, such that $3^n \equiv 1 \pmod{1000}$—because when you take a number mod 1000 you get the last three digits of the number. But, the pigeonhole principle doesn't tell us what the exponent n is; it just proves that n exists somewhere. Euler's theorem can actually tell us what n is. Let's apply Euler's theorem with the numbers $a = 3$ and $m = 1000$; those are legal values because 3 and 1000 are relatively prime. What's ϕ of 1000? By the formula we developed, ϕ of 1000 would be $1000 \times (1 - 1/2) \times (1 - 1/5)$, which equals 400. Therefore, Euler's theorem promises that $3^{400} \equiv 1 \pmod{1000}$; just plugging right into Euler's theorem. Therefore, 3^{400} ends in 001. There's nothing special about the number 3 in this proof anywhere. Any number that's not divisible by 2 or 5, that is, any number that's relatively prime to 1000, is going to have this property.

In Lecture One, we proved that 2009 divides a number consisting of all 9s, although we didn't know how many 9s were in it. Euler's theorem shows that this is true for any number that's not divisible by 2 or 5, and it tells you how many 9s are in the answer. Here's what Euler's theorem gives us: Let m be any number that does not divide by 2 or 5. In other words, let m be relatively prime to 10. By Euler's theorem, if I let $a = 10$ and I let $m = m$, then Euler's theorem says that $10^{\phi(m)} \equiv 1 \pmod{m}$. In other words, by the definition of modular arithmetic, m divides $10^{\phi(m)} - 1$. If you take 10 to a power and then subtract 1, what do you get? You've got a number consisting of all 9s, like $10^3 - 1$ is 999. In general, $10^{\phi(m)} - 1$ is going to have, how many 9s in it? Whatever the exponent was, $\phi(m)$. Since 2009 is $7 \times 7 \times 41$, we can find ϕ of 2009; ϕ of 2009 will be 1680. Therefore, 2009 divides a number consisting of all 9s, in fact, exactly 1680 of those 9s.

Euler's theorem can sometimes help us raise numbers to enormous powers. For example, let's say I want to calculate 6^{83} (mod 79). Since 6 and 79 are relatively prime, so I can use Euler's theorem here. What's $\phi(79)$? [Since] 79 is prime and ϕ of a prime number is that prime -1, ϕ of 79 is 78. Euler's theorem, letting $a = 6$ and $m = 79$, tells us that $6^{78} \equiv$ to 1 (mod 79). But of course, the problem I asked you was 6^{83}. Well, 6^{83} is $6^{78} \times 6^5$. The $6^{78} = 1$ (mod 79); it disappears mod 79, so we're left with 6^5, which is 7776, which as we've seen before is congruent to 34 (mod 79). Here's another question: What's $6^{78,005}$ (mod 79)? Again, $6^{78,000}$ is $(6^{78})^{1000}$, but 6^{78} disappears mod 79, giving us 6^5, the same answer as before— 34 (mod 79).

We'll turn to more serious applications of Euler's theorem when we do public key cryptography in our next lecture. Meanwhile, let's explore some more applications of Fermat's theorem. Fermat's theorem says: If p is prime, then $a^p \equiv a$ (mod p). In other words, if n is prime, then $a^n \equiv a$ (mod n). For example, when a is 2 and n is 5— 2^5 is 32—[which] is congruent to 2 (mod 5). When n is 7, it predicts that $2^7 \equiv 2$ (mod 7), and it is. As we've seen before, $2^{11} \equiv 2$ (mod 11). But when n is 9, 2^9 is 512, which we know is congruent to 8 (mod 9), and that is not congruent to 2. What conclusion do we make from that? We conclude from that that 9 is not prime because if 9 were prime, 2^9 would be congruent to 2 (mod 9).

It's this idea that forms the cornerstone of prime testing. It's basically the contrapositive of Fermat's theorem. Fermat's theorem says: If n is prime, then $a^n \equiv a$ (mod n). Contrapositively, this is equivalent to saying: If a^n is not congruent to a (mod n), then n is not prime. In other words, the contrapositive gives us compositeness. This test is known as the Fermat primality test. If a^n is not congruent to a (mod n), then n is composite. This gives us an unusual way to check that a number is composite without having to factor it. Let's say we're given a big number, let's say a 100-digit number n, and we compute 2^n (mod n). We know how to do that from our last lecture. If 2^n (mod n) is not equal to 2, then n is not prime. If 2^n (mod n) is equal to 2, then n is probably prime, but we can't be sure. This is sometimes called an "industrial-grade prime"; the more standard name is a "base-2 pseudo-prime."

Alas, some composite numbers are base-2 pseudo-primes. The first one is 341, which we can use seed planting or the lucky method to show satisfies $2^{341} \equiv 2$ (mod 341). Even though it isn't prime, it's acting like a prime, so 341 would be a base-2 pseudo-prime that was composite. The next one is 561. To be safe, we could see if 3^n (mod n) is equal to 3, and that would weed out 341; 341 doesn't satisfy; it is not a base-3 pseudo-prime, but it doesn't weed out 561. As a matter of fact, $a^{561} \equiv a$ (mod 561) for all values of a, even though 561 is not prime. It really wants to be prime, but it's not. It's $3 \times 11 \times 17$.

These kinds of numbers are called annoying, frankly. But the mathematical name for them is "Carmichael numbers." Good news: Carmichael numbers are rare; 561 is the only one under 1000. The next two are 1105 and a very interesting number, 1729. The bad news is there are infinitely many of them. That was proved only recently, in 1994, by Alford, Granville, and Pomerance. The good news is Fermat's test can be modified to avoid them.

In our next lecture, we'll apply what we've learned about prime testing and Euler's theorem to provide a way for doing public key cryptography, an extremely relevant application based on very elegant mathematics.

Lecture Fifteen
Open Secrets—Public Key Cryptography

Scope:

Suppose that to encode a secret message, you take every letter of your message and shift the letter forward by 3 letters. For instance, the word CAT would become FDW. Then when someone receives the secret message, it is a simple matter to reverse the procedure by shifting each letter backward by 3 letters. With public key cryptography, however, everyone knows how the messages get encoded, yet only the recipient knows how to reverse the procedure. This idea is one of the ways Internet commerce remains secure. We will explore the RSA method for doing public key cryptography.

Outline

I. Public key cryptography (from the Greek roots "crypto" and "graphon," meaning "hidden writing") is perhaps the most discreet application of discrete mathematics.

  A. Suppose I have a secret message that I want to send to you, say, "quiz today." This message is known as the plaintext since it could be read plainly by anyone. How can we disguise our message?

  B. One of the simplest codes to create (and break) is the shift method, where every letter is shifted by the same amount. For example if the amount of our shift (known as the key) was to shift every letter forward by 2 (mod 26), then "quiz today" would become "swkb vqfca," known as the ciphertext.

  C. Someone reading the ciphertext could not easily determine the plaintext. But if the recipients know the key, they can easily determine the plaintext by shifting every letter backward by 2.

  D. The idea behind public key cryptography sounds impossible. Imagine that a bank wants anyone in the world to be able to communicate with it over the Internet in a secure way. The bank posts on its website, for everyone to see, a public key.

E. Here is how it works: On the privacy of your computer, you convert the plaintext into ciphertext using the bank's public key. Then you e-mail the ciphertext to the bank (very insecure). But despite the fact that everyone knows the public key, only the bank can decipher the message.

II. The most famous method for public key cryptography is called the RSA method.

   A. It was named after 3 mathematically trained computer scientists, Ronald Rivest, Adi Shamier, and Leonard Adleman, who discovered this method in 1977.

   B. Let a, b, and n be enormous numbers (say 2000 digits long). It is very easy for a computer to calculate a^b mod n and $\gcd(a, b)$ and to determine if n is a prime number. But if n is composite—say, $n = pq$, where p and q are 1000-digit primes—then it is very hard for a computer to factor n.

   C. Here is how RSA works: The bank publishes 2 numbers on its website, n and e (as in "encipher"); n and e are about 2000 digits long.

   1. Write your plaintext (under 1000 characters). Example: plaintext = QuizToday.

   2. Covert plaintext to a number M (under 2000 digits) by replacing each letter with its 2-digit position in the alphabet. For example, QuizToday becomes 172109262015040125.

   3. Computer ciphertext $C = M^e$ mod n. You e-mail C to the bank.

   4. When the bank receives C, it uses a magic secret number d (as in "decipher") and computes C^d mod n, which (amazingly) equals M. Then it converts M back to plaintext.

   D. How are d, e, and n chosen?

   1. The bank secretly chooses 2 random 1000-digit primes, p and q, and computes $n = pq$. The product n is made public, but the primes p and q are kept private.

   2. The bank computes $\phi(n) = (p - 1)(q - 1)$, then selects a random 1000-digit number d that is relatively prime to $\phi(n)$, using the Euclidean algorithm.

3. Since $(d, \phi(n)) = 1$, Euclid's algorithm finds positive integers e and f such that $de - \phi(n)f = 1$. The number d is kept private, but the number e is made public.

III. We work through a numerical example using small prime numbers.

A. Say $p = 71$ and $q = 79$, so that $n = pq = 5609$ and $\phi(n) = (p-1)(q-1) = 70 \times 78 = 5460$. We chose $d = 341$, which is relatively prime to 5460.

B. Euclid's algorithm verifies that $(5460, 341) = 1$ and finds the integer combination $341(1361) - 5460(85) = 1$, so $e = 1361$.

C. To send the message "Hi," we let $M = 0809$. We send $C = M^e \pmod{n} = (809)^{1361} \bmod 5609 = 4394$.

D. The bank deciphers our message by computing $(4394)^{341} \bmod 5609$, which equals 809, which the bank converts to the plaintext "Hi."

E. If both the bank and the customer have their own public key numbers, then the customer has a way of providing digital signatures so that the bank can trust that the message came from the customer. With digital signatures, not only was the customer the only one who could send the message, but the signature is also message specific, so it cannot be forged or attached to a different message.

Suggested Reading:

Scheinerman, *Mathematics: A Discrete Introduction*, secs. 43, 45.

Silverman, *A Friendly Introduction to Number Theory*, chap. 18.

Questions to Consider:

1. If n is a composite number, why must it have a divisor larger than 1 that is no bigger than $\sqrt{n}$?

2. In the RSA method of public key cryptography, with $p = 17$ and $q = 29$, what is the chance that a numerical message M (with $0 \leq M < 493$) would not be relatively prime to $n = pq = 493$?

3. For the RSA problem with $p = 17$ and $q = 29$, suppose that the bank publishes the enciphering number $e = 303$. What secret number d does the bank use to decipher its messages?

4. Do the same problem with $p = 71$, $q = 79$, and $e = 101$.

5. Here is how digital signatures work. Suppose that the bank has public key numbers e and n (with secret number d) and that you also have public key numbers $e*$ and $n*$ (with secret number $d*$). To send a "signed" message M to the bank, begin by computing $C = M^e$ (mod n), but then compute $C* = C^{d*}$(mod $n*$), and send the message $C*$ to the bank, along with an unencrypted note that this message is coming from you. How does the bank decipher your message?

Lecture Fifteen—Transcript
Open Secrets—Public Key Cryptography

The word cryptography comes from the Greek words *crypto*, meaning "hidden," and *grapho*, meaning "writing." People have practiced the art of cryptography—hidden writing—for about as long as people have been able to write. You might say that cryptography is the most discreet application of discrete mathematics.

Suppose I have a secret message that I want to send to you. Let's say it says, QUIZ TODAY. This message is known as the "plaintext" since it could be read plainly by anyone. Now, how could we disguise our message? One of the simplest codes to create and break is the shift method, where every letter is shifted by the same amount. For instance, my key might be to shift every letter forward by 2. But, of course, when I shift it by 2, I'm referring to that mod 26. For instance, the Q, when I shift it forward by 2, would become an S; the U would become a W; the I would become a K; and the Z, when I shift that forward by 2, would become a B. Then, with "today," T would become a V, O would become Q, D would become F, A would be C, and Y—when I add 2 to it mod 26—I go to Z and then to A. This message here is called our "cipher text" because somebody just looking at that wouldn't be able to make sense out of it. Someone reading the cipher text wouldn't easily determine it, but if the recipient knows the key, then they can easily determine the plaintext by shifting every letter backwards by 2.

Of course, there are more sophisticated codes out there, but here's a simple code that is 100 percent unbreakable. It's called "white noise," and it's undoubtedly used for the most sensitive communication—say, between the White House and the Kremlin. Here's how it works: At the beginning of the year, the White House sends, by trusted courier, a file called "the key" with millions and millions and millions of random digits. Those random digits are numbers between 1 and 26. For instance, suppose our key begins—oh, I don't know—3 14 15 9 26 5 3 5 8, whatever random digits you want. They should be more random then that, by the way. Then, given the plaintext QUIZ TODAY, we would shift the first letter by 3, and the second letter by 14, and so on to get this mixed-up little cipher text. That's something that would be impossible to decipher unless you know the key. The recipient knows the key and can decipher it easily by shifting those letters back 3, then 14, then 15, then 9, and so on. But anyone else who sees the cipher text really has no clue what the plaintext is.

The reason they have absolutely no clue is because the key was random, or it should be. Don't use digits of π or something popular like that; use random digits because with random digits, the plaintext that generated it could have been literally anything else. Let's say my message, instead of being QUIZ TODAY, was MATH ROCKS. That could have also generated the cipher text, that same cipher text, with the exact same probability. By the way, for complete security, once the first message is sent, those first nine numbers in the key should be thrown away and not reused because otherwise that could be exploited.

White noise has its drawbacks. First of all, trusted couriers can get expensive. Second, if the key were ever made public, then the cipher text could be read by anyone. The idea behind public key cryptography actually sounds impossible. Imagine that a bank wants you or anyone in the world to be able to communicate with it over the Internet, without having to use a trusted courier. The bank posts on its Web site, for the world to see, a public key. The Web site might look like this; here we are at Zurich National Bank, and it says, "Hi, you want to send us a safe message? Just follow these three easy steps." On the privacy of your computer, you convert the plaintext into cipher text using the bank's public key—and we'll see examples of that shortly—then you e-mail the cipher text to the bank.

That's very insecure. I've heard it said that sending an e-mail is about as private as mailing a postcard; many eyes could potentially see it, so you don't want to send anything that's very confidential by e-mail. But despite the fact that everyone in the world knows the bank's public key, only the bank can decipher the message. Doesn't that sound impossible? Here's you, you take your plaintext, and you convert it somehow into the cipher text using the steps that the bank tells you to do. Then, once you have the cipher text, you send the cipher text across the Internet, across cyberspace, to the bank's computer. Then the bank, using just a little bit of extra information, figures out what your plaintext is. The public key cryptography method that we're going to use is known as the RSA method, named after three mathematically trained computer scientists, Rivest, Shamir, and Adleman, who discovered this method in 1977. By the way, MIT held a patent on the RSA method until 2000, when it was released into public domain.

Here's how the RSA method works: Let a, b, and n be enormous numbers. When I say enormous, I want you to think numbers that are like 2000 digits long. You're not going to be doing this by hand, but your computer won't have trouble with it. What do we know so far about computational number theory? We've learned that it's very easy for a computer to calculate—even with 2000-digit numbers, like a, b, and n—that your computer can calculate a^b (mod n); it knows how to do that. It also knows how to calculate the greatest common divisor of a and b. We saw that Euclid's algorithm is fast, so even with [numbers] thousands of digits long, it can do that in just a few thousand steps. We also know, using Fermat's test, we can tell if the number n is a prime number or any number, for that matter. We can tell if it's prime in a reasonable amount of time, using seed planting and Fermat's test. That's what we can do that's easy. Here's the hard part: If n is a composite number, let's say n is pq, where p and q are 1000-digit primes, then it's very hard for a computer or anyone to factor the number n. In other words, find those numbers p and q that created n; that's hard. Prime testing, exponentiation, greatest common divisors—those are easy. Factoring is hard.

By the way, the simplest algorithm for factoring a number—trial division—let me just give you a sense as to how hard it is; [it] takes about $\sqrt{n}$ steps. You'd say, "Well, let's divide it by 2; does it work?" If it doesn't, try 3, try 5, try 7, try 11, you know, try all the numbers—at least all the prime numbers—up to $\sqrt{n}$, and if you don't find any divisors up through $\sqrt{n}$, then you know your number's prime. How long will that take? If n is about 10^{2000}—in other words, if n is a 2000-digit number, like 10^{2000}—then $\sqrt{n}$ is 10^{1000}. In other words, trial division would take you about n^{1000}. The fastest known algorithms take about, instead of $n^{1/2}$, about $n^{1/4}$, in other words, $\sqrt{\sqrt{n}}$ steps. One method, called Pollard's method, takes that. If n was about 10^{2000}, it would find it in about 10^{500}.

The fastest algorithms take, at current state of the art, about $e^{\sqrt{(\ln n)\ln \ln n}}$ —isn't that a crazy expression? For this number, it would take about e^{197} steps, or about 10^{85} steps. Just to give you an idea how big 10^{85} is, how long would that take? If your computer could do a trillion calculations per second, then it would take more than a trillion, trillion, trillion, trillion, trillion years to solve the problem.

This reminds me of a joke: What does a drowning number theorist say? Log, log, log, log, log, log, log, log, log—but I digress. Here is how the RSA method works: First, we'll learn how, then we'll learn why. The bank publishes two numbers on its Web site, n (the big number) and e (e as in "encipher"). [The numbers] n and e are both like 2000 digits long. You write your plaintext, and your plaintext has to be, let's say, under 1000 characters because each of those characters might take up two digits, so you want your message to be under 2000 digits long.

Write your plaintext in under 1000 characters. For example, if the plaintext said, QUIZ TODAY, then you would convert this to a number; we'll call that number M, and that number M will be under 2000 digits long. Here's how we would do it: We would take the QUIZ—Q becomes 17, U becomes 21, I becomes 09, Z becomes 26, and so on. So M would be that 18-digit number—QUIZ TODAY becomes this 18-digit number. By the way, if your message was more than 1000 characters long, then you'd just have to do this process more than one time. Next, you take your 18-digit number, M, your message, and you raise it to the e power—e as in "encipher"— mod n, and we can do that. It's a big number, raised to a big power, mod a big modulus, and we can do that, and we get our cipher text, which we call C. What is C? It's just a number that's less than n. It's the remainder when you divide M^e by n. It's less than 2000 digits long. We're going to take that number C, and we're going to e-mail it to the bank over cyberspace. Anyone in the world, our worst enemy, could see what C is. When the bank receives C, it uses a magic secret number, which I'll call d, as in "decipher," and it computes $C^d \pmod{n}$, and magically, $C^d \pmod{n}$ is going to equal the number M, which the bank then converts M to the plaintext QUIZ TODAY. Doesn't that sound like magic?

Let me say it one more time; let's summarize what we have. Starting with your numerical message M, you compute the cipher text C by calculating $M^e \pmod{n}$. Then, the bank, using its secret number d, computes $C^d \pmod{n}$, and magically, out pops M. That's all it is. That's the RSA method. But I haven't told you yet how n, d, and e are chosen. Here's how to choose the numbers. The bank secretly chooses two random 1000-digit prime numbers. We'll call those numbers p and q; p and q are prime numbers about 1000 digits long. Now you may ask: How does it find a 1000-digit prime? Does it go on the Internet and look for popular 1000 digit primes? No, these have to be ultra-secret. What the bank does is it randomly generates a 1000-digit number and then tests to see if that number is prime. Once it has a prime, it has a secret prime for life that nobody has probably ever seen before. There are plenty of 1000-digit prime numbers out there; the prime number theorem tells us how many there are. In fact, according to the prime number theorem, which we saw in Lecture Ten, that the number of prime numbers less than or equal to n is approximately n divided by the natural log of n, or n divided by about 2.3 times the base-10 logarithm of n.

What that means is roughly one in every 2300 numbers is prime when you're looking at numbers in the vicinity of 10^{1000}. If you make sure that you always choose a number that isn't even and isn't a multiple of 5, just by tweaking that last digit, then there's about a 1 in 1000 chance that this random 1000-digit number that you've picked is prime. You can test for its primeness pretty efficiently, using Fermat's test and its variations. If it is prime, great; you're done. If it's not prime, try again, and if that's not prime, try again. It should only take you about 1000, maybe 2000 attempts before you find your own secret prime p, and then you do that process again to find another secret prime, q. You have p and q, they are these 1000-digit primes, and you multiply them together to get your number n; n is going to be about 2000 digits, and that's going to be made public for the world to see, but the bank keeps p and q private, so everybody knows n, but only the bank knows p and q.

Next, the bank computes $\phi(n)$; $\phi(n)$ was the number that we used in Euler's theorem. We know that if n is equal to pq, then $\phi(n)$—that is, $\phi(pq)$—is going to equal $\phi(p)\phi(q)$, because p and q are relatively prime. That's $(p-1)(q-1)$. The bank can easily figure out what $\phi(n)$ is. The bank then secretly chooses a random 1000-digit number d that is relatively prime to $\phi(n)$. How does it do that? It takes this 1000-digit number d, and it does the Euclidean algorithm with $\phi(n)$, and if you get 1 when you're done, then they're relatively prime. If not, try it again. Euclid's algorithm won't complain, it's very fast, and it won't take more than a handful of tries before you find a number d that's relatively prime to $\phi(n)$. Since d and $\phi(n)$ are relatively prime, we know from Bezout's theorem that Euclid's algorithm will find us positive integers e and f, so that $de - \phi(n)f$ gives us 1. It finds an integer combination of d and $\phi(n)$ that gives us 1.

Let me summarize. If n is equal to pq, how do we choose d, e, and M? [The number] n is equal to pq where p and q are secret 1000-digit primes; d is also a secret 1000-digit number that's relatively prime to $\phi(n)$. Euclid finds positive integers e and f so that $de - \phi(n)f = 1$, and the bank makes e, the enciphering number, public, so anybody can see it. The theorem of the day is that RSA—this magical process—actually works. In other words, if you take your message M, and you raise it to the e power (mod n), and you get your cipher text C, then when the bank takes your cipher text C and raises it to the d power—the deciphering exponent—(mod n), out pops your message M. I'll say it again; our theorem is that if M^e (mod n) = C, then C^d (mod n) = M.

Let's prove it. First, we'll make a few elementary observations, and we'll build on these elementary observations. Do you agree with the fact that C^d (mod n) $\equiv C^d$ (mod n)? It almost sounds like a tautology, right? Are you saying anything at all? Yes, I'm saying if you take the number C^d, and you look at its remainder when you divide it by n, that's going to have the same remainder as C^d when you divide it by n. It's really a very quick observation. Also, M^e (mod n) $\equiv M^e$ (mod n). But those two numbers differ by a multiple of n.

With that as our background, let's begin the proof of the RSA theorem. If M^e (mod n) = C, I want to show that C^d (mod n) = M. Therefore, working with modulus n—all those congruences are modulus n—we have C^d (mod n) $\equiv C^d$. Eventually, I want to get M out of this—and C^d, I can replace C with M^e (mod n)^d. But, M^e (mod n) $\equiv M^e$ (mod n). I can replace the M^e (mod n) with the M^e. Can we really do that? Doesn't that exponent d mess things up? No, by the power theorem, if $a \equiv b$, then $a^d \equiv b^d$, so we're safe. Now, $(M^e)^d$, that's a number, and by the law of exponents, that's M^{ed}. But what do we know about ed? By the Bezout relationship that Euclid found for us, remember, $de - \phi(n)f = 1$. I can replace ed with the number $1 + \phi(n)f$, just algebraically making that substitution.

By the law of exponents, that's $M^1 \times M^{\phi(n)f}$—just taking little algebraic steps here. Now M^1, that's just M; $M^{\phi(n)f}$, by the law of exponents again, that's $(M^{\phi(n)})^f$. But Euler's theorem jumps into the game and says, "Wait a second; I know that $M^{\phi(n)} \equiv 1$ (mod n)"— isn't that that Euler's theorem? [Remember,] $M^{\phi(n)} \equiv 1$ (mod n), so when I put on my mod n glasses, that $M^{\phi(n)}$ just looks like a measly little 1. So $(M^{\phi(n)})^f$, by the power law, looks like 1^f, and 1^f is 1, so I can ignore that to get M.

What we've shown here is that $C^d \pmod{n}$ is, following that chain of equal signs and congruences, $C^d \pmod{n} \equiv M \pmod{n}$. But hold on; I didn't want to say congruent. I wanted to actually get equals out of this. But we're in luck because $C^d \pmod{n}$ is some number between 0 and n, and our message M, if you remember, that had to be a number between 0 and n. That's why we said our message had to be under 1000 characters long—less than 2000 digits long. If two numbers are congruent mod n, but they both live between 0 and n, they have to be the same number. Therefore, $C^d \pmod{n} = M$.

You may need to run through this proof once or twice before it fully sinks in, but that's it. That is practically everything you need to know, except for the fact that I cheated, but just a little. Remember the step where I pulled in Euler's theorem? I said, wait a second folks, I said $M^{\phi(n)} \equiv 1 \pmod{n}$? Remember that? You have to also remember there's a preamble to Euler's theorem. In order to use it, you need M and n to be relatively prime, right? How do I know that M and n are relatively prime? What would happen if M and n weren't relatively prime?

First of all, what can the greatest common divisor of M and n be? What is the number n, after all? [The number] n is pq; it's the product of these prime numbers p and q. What are the divisors of p and q? What are the divisors of pq? [They are] 1, p, q, and pq; that's it, and n is less than pq, so the greatest common divisor will either be 1, or p, or q. Can it be p or q? Technically, it's possible, but the probability that M is a multiple of p is about 1 in p, and the probability that M is a multiple of q is about 1 in q. The probability that it's a multiple of p or a multiple of q is about 1 in $p + 1$ in q, and I claim that's 0. Really, p and q are numbers like 10^{1000} power, so the probability that your number is a multiple of p or q—you would be more likely to be struck like lightning and win the lottery on your birthday.

You probably want to see a numerical example, so let's do a small one. Let's say p is 71—our secret prime number that nobody knows about: p is 71 and q is 79, so n is $p \times q = 5609$. Everyone in the world knows 5609, but nobody knows how to factor it. Only the bank knows how to factor it. Then, the bank calculates ϕ of n, which is $p - 1 \times q - 1$. That's $70 \times 78 = 5460$. The bank says, [we] need a secret number that's relatively prime to 5460. That's 60×91, so that's divisible by 60, 2, 3, 5; 91 is 7×13. We just have to find a number that doesn't have any of those prime factors in it. I chose the number 341, because 341 is 31×11, and that doesn't have any factors in common with 5460. Euclid's algorithm is smart. It calculates an integer combination of 341 and 5460. We get it right here: $341 \times 1361, -5460 \times 85 = 1$, so we found our e—namely, 1361. That's the enciphering number that the world is allowed to see. We have n is 5609 (that's public); d is 341 (that's private); e is 1361.

Now, let's say we want to send a short message to the bank, like HI. What do we do with HI? H-I is the eighth letter and the ninth letter of the alphabet, so our message M would be 0809. Notice that number is less than n, our modulus, 5609, so that's a valid message. Then, to create the cipher text C, we raise M to the e power (mod n). We take the number 809 [and] raise it to the 1361st power (mod 5609). Since our computer knows how to do seed planting, it can actually do that calculation easily. That's equal to 4394. The bank will decipher our message by taking 4394, raising it to its deciphering number, 341, (mod n)—(mod 5609)—and sure enough, out pops 809. The bank knows that we've sent [the message] HI.

Incidentally, if both the bank and the customer have their own public key cryptosystem, then the customer actually has a way of providing digital signatures so that the bank can trust that the message actually came from the customer. Not only do digital signatures work, but the message that you send, the message that the bank receives, is un-forgeable, so the bank can figure out that only you were the one capable of sending the message. Just as importantly, your signature is message specific, so your signature can't be forged or attached to a different message, nor can you claim that you sent a different message.

Wow, look at all these applications: We've got public key cryptography. We have digital signatures. What would Hardy say to all of this? By the way, there's another neat connection between Euler and Fermat that I'd like to tell you about. In the year 1729, when Euler was 22 years old, Christian Goldbach—you remember him from Goldbach's conjecture—posed another conjecture to Euler that was given by Fermat. Fermat observed that the numbers $2^{2^0} + 1 = 3$; and $2^{2^1} + 1 = 5$; and $2^{2^2} + 1$, that's $2^4 + 1$, is 17; and $2^{2^3} + 1$, that's $2^8 + 1$, is 257; and $2^{2^4} + 1$, $2^{16} + 1$, [is] 65,537. He noticed that all of those numbers were prime. He conjectured that $2^{2^n} + 1$ would always be prime.

At the time, Euler was not so interested in number theory. It was somewhat unfashionable [in] those days for mathematicians to demean themselves with the study of numbers, but he was intrigued by this problem. After thinking about it, he disproved Fermat's conjecture by exhibiting a counterexample. He showed that $2^{2^5} + 1$ actually was composite. That is, it's $6{,}700{,}417 \times 641$; my understanding was that he did most of that in his head, too. No other Fermat primes have been found beyond those first 5, so that's kind of interesting. Not only was Fermat wrong, [but] he seemed to be wrong in a very big way. But this sparked a lifelong interest in number theory by Euler.

Gauss, by the way, was also inspired by Fermat numbers. He was the first to construct a regular 17-sided polygon using ruler and compass, and this was an open question from Euclid—a 2000-year-old problem [that] he solved. He noticed that 17 was a Fermat prime, and he stated that a regular n-gon could be constructed using ruler and compass if n is of the form 2^m (some number m) × the product of a bunch of distinct Fermat primes. This sparked his interest in staying on in mathematics instead of pursuing another subject. Anyway, Goldbach's letter to Euler was written in 1729—and that's also interesting, which brings the mathematician Hardy into the picture.

This is a classical story, a famous story: Hardy was visiting a collaborator of his, Srinivasa Ramanujan, a self-taught Indian mathematical genius of the highest order. He was visiting Ramanujan in the hospital one day. To make small talk he said, "You know, the taxi ride was kind of dull. The number on the taxi was 1729 (the year of Goldbach's letter), and I couldn't think of anything mathematically interesting about it." Ramanujan said, "Oh no, Hardy, it's a very interesting number. It's the first number that can be written as the sum of two positive-numbered cubes in two different ways. That is, it's $10^3 + 9^3$, and it's also $12^3 + 1^3$.

We may not all have the genius of Ramanujan, but I hope that we've learned to appreciate numbers in a whole new light. We've seen that numbers are far more interesting and far more applicable than Hardy, Ramanujan, Gauss, Fermat, Euler, or Euclid ever imagined.

Lecture Sixteen
The Birth of Graph Theory

Scope:

In this lecture, we introduce the subject of graph theory, an extremely useful branch of discrete mathematics, with beautiful theorems and myriad applications. In graph theory, objects are represented by vertices (dots or points) in space, and 2 vertices are connected by an edge (or line) if the objects are related in some way. We establish the basic definitions and notation and prove some of the basic theorems. We define walks, paths, trails, and cycles and then prove the first theorem of graph theory, due to Euler.

Outline

I. The first concepts of graph theory include walks, paths, trails, and cycles.

  A. Although the first theorem of graph theory goes back to 1736, it is a very modern subject. Its first textbook appeared in 1958, and research journals in graph theory are less than 40 years old.

  B. Although we usually think of a graph by its picture, the formal definition describes a graph in terms of sets and subsets. A graph G consists of a finite vertex set V and an edge set E consisting of size-2 subsets of V.

  C. For example, the graph G pictured here

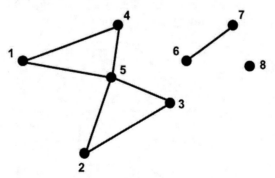

  has $V = \{1, 2, 3, 4, 5, 6, 7, 8\}$ and $E = \{\{1,4\}, \{1, 5\}, \{2, 3\}, \{2, 5\}, \{3, 5\}, \{4, 5\}, \{6, 7\}\}$.

D. A graph does not allow an edge to go from a vertex to itself (known as a loop), nor does it allow more than 1 edge to connect a pair of vertices (known as multiedges). When we want our graph to allow multiple edges, we call it a multigraph.

E. If an edge exists between x and y, then we say that x and y are adjacent. For example, in our pictured graph G, vertices 3 and 5 are adjacent.

F. The number of vertices adjacent to vertex v is called the degree of v, denoted $d(v)$. For example, $d(1) = 2$, $d(5) = 4$, and $d(8) = 0$.

G. There are various ways to "walk" along a graph.

  1. A walk on a graph is a sequence of adjacent vertices where repetition is allowed. For example, $W = 1, 5, 2, 3, 5, 3, 5$ is a walk of length 6 from 1 to 5.

  2. A path is a walk with no repeated vertices. For example, $P = 1, 5, 2, 3$ is a path from 1 to 3. Notice that if a walk exists from x to y, then a path exists from x to y.

  3. A trail is a walk with no repeated edges. For example, 1, 5, 2, 3, 5, 4 is a trail, and so is 1, 5, 2, 3, 5, 4. A trail is closed if it begins and ends with the same vertex.

  4. A cycle (of length k) is a closed trail $v_0, v_1, \ldots, v_k$ (note that $v_k = v_0$), such that $v_0, v_1, \ldots, v_{k-1}$ is a path.

H. A graph is connected if for all vertices x and y, there is a path from x to y.

II. Leonhard Euler invented graph theory in order to solve what is the oldest theorem of graph theory.

  A. Question: Can you draw this graph without lifting your pen off the paper and without retracing any edges?

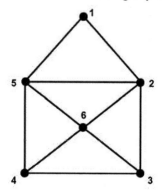

B. Yes, and here's one way to do it: 3, 6, 5, 2, 6, 4, 5, 1, 2, 3, 4.

   1. Such a graph is called drawable. If we remove the 2 edges at the top ($\{1, 2\}$ and $\{1, 5\}$), then the graph is no longer drawable, since a trail from x to y that uses every edge must enter and exit every vertex (except x and y) an even number of times. Hence, such a graph must have at most 2 vertices of odd degree. Since this graph would have 4 vertices of odd degree, it would not be drawable.

   2. Note that in the original graph, there are exactly 2 vertices of odd degree (vertices 3 and 4), so any trail that draws the graph must have endpoints 3 and 4. The altered graph cannot be drawn in such a way that it begins and ends at the same point, since that would require that every vertex have even degree.

C. We say that a graph (or multigraph) is Eulerian if it is connected and G contains a closed trail that uses every edge.

D. By our earlier argument, we see that if G is Eulerian, then G is connected and every vertex must have even degree. The converse statement is also true. The Eulerian graph theorem: If G is connected and every vertex has even degree, then G is Eulerian.

E. Eulerian graphs have applications outside of graph drawing. For example, they can be used to create de Bruijn sequences, where all 2^n binary code words of length n can be encapsulated in a single list of 2^n numbers.

F. Eulerian graphs should not be confused with Hamiltonian graphs. A graph is Hamiltonian if it contains a cycle that goes through every vertex (but might not use every edge).

Suggested Reading:

Chartrand, *Introductory Graph Theory*, chaps. 1, 3.

Hopkins and Wilson, "The Truth about Königsberg."

Lovász, Pelikán, and Vesztergombi, *Discrete Mathematics*, chap. 7.

Rosen, *Discrete Mathematics and Its Applications*, chap. 8.

Scheinerman, *Mathematics: A Discrete Introduction*, secs. 46, 50.

West, *Introduction to Graph Theory*.

Questions to Consider:

1. For the graph G presented below:

    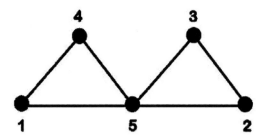

    a. Give the vertex set and edge set for G.

    b. Find the shortest path from vertex 1 to vertex 3.

    c. Is G Eulerian?

    d. Is G Hamiltonian?

2. Recall that the complete graph K_n contains n vertices and that every pair of vertices is connected by an edge.

    a. How many edges does the complete graph K_n have?

    b. Prove that for $n \geq 3$, K_n is Eulerian if and only if n is odd.

3. Using the Eulerian graph theorem, prove that if G is a connected graph with exactly 2 vertices of odd degree, say, vertices x and y, then G can be drawn as a trail from x to y.

4. Let G_1 and G_2 be Eulerian graphs with no vertices in common. Let x be a vertex in G_1; let y be a vertex in G_2; and let G be the graph obtained by connecting G_1 and G_2 with an edge from x to y. What can you say about the new graph?

5. **a.** Draw the graph of a cube. It will have 8 vertices and 12 edges.

    b. Is this graph Eulerian?

    c. Is this graph Hamiltonian?

Lecture Sixteen—Transcript
The Birth of Graph Theory

We now begin our last major component of this course, graph theory. Although the first theorem of graph theory goes back to 1736, it's a very modern subject. Its first textbook appeared in 1958, and research journals and graph theory are under 40 years old.

We usually think of a graph by its picture. Here is a typical graph. The formal definition of a graph is: It's a finite vertex set V and an edge set E containing size-2 subsets of V, which is very hard to digest, but I have to give it out because it's the official definition. For example, the graph you're looking at—your computer, if it were staring at the graph, would see eight vertices labeled with the numbers 1 through 8 (so that's the vertex set), and it would see seven edges, and the edges would be the set 1, 4; 1, 5; 2, 3; 2, 5; 3, 5; 4, 5; and 6, 7. Those would be the edges represented. See, it's not that bad a definition.

By our definition, a graph does not contain any loops or multiple edges between two vertices; here's a non-example of a graph. Here, for instance, is a loop that begins and ends at 2—that's not allowed—and here, between vertices 3 and 4, I have three edges, so those would be multiple edges; that's not allowed in our graph either. If we want to allow multiple edges to exist between some vertices, then we call it a "multigraph" instead of a graph. We'll use multigraphs occasionally in this course.

For example, an airline may have several flights that go between the same pair of cities. For such a situation, we may prefer to use a multigraph. As a matter of fact, the formal definition of multigraph is the same as the definition for a graph, but instead of using a subset of edges, we're using a multi-subset of edges.

If an edge exists between x and y, then we say that the vertices x and y are "adjacent." For example, in our graph G, just looking at the picture, the vertices 3 and 5 are adjacent. The number of vertices adjacent to a vertex v is called the "degree of v" and it's denoted by d of v For example, the degree of vertex 1 is 2, because it's adjacent to vertices 4 and 5; the degree of 5 is 4. The degree of vertex 8, sitting all by itself, is 0.

In this lecture, we will encounter the oldest theorem in graph theory, which is over 270 years old. Yet since most of the research on the subject of graph theory has only been conducted in the last several decades, the definitions often have a friendly, modern sound to them. For instance, in this lecture, we'll encounter definitions like "walks," "paths," "trails," and "cycles." In later lectures, we'll encounter such things as "tournaments," "trees," "forests," "leaves," and "proper colorings."

How would you define a walk on a graph? Again, here's our graph. What would a walk be? We'll define a walk on a graph to be a sequence of adjacent vertices, where repetition is allowed. But I just think of it as bopping from one point to another, with no restrictions given whatsoever. We can start at 1, and then go to 5, and then go to 2, and then go to 3, and then to 5, then to 3 again, then to 5 again. That's a walk; it's a walk of length of 6 because I took 6 steps along the way. Anything goes. That's a walk from 1 to 5. On the other hand, a path is a walk where no vertices are allowed to be repeated. For example, here, the path that goes from 1 to 5 to 2 to 3, this is a path from vertex 1 to vertex 3.

Here's an observation: If a walk exists from x to y, then a path must exist from x to y. For instance, in this graph here, here was a walk from vertex 1 to vertex 4; it went from 1 to 5 to 2 to 3 to 5 to 4. But any walk that includes repeated vertices can still get to its destination without using repeated vertices; you just cut out that cycle as soon as you enter it. Here would be a shorter walk from 1 to 4. A definition: A graph is connected if, for all vertices x and y, there is a path that gets us from x to y. It's the intuitive definition. If you looked at this graph here in the picture and I asked: Is this graph connected? Just looking at it, you'd say yes. Whereas the next graph, the graph G here, is that connected? No, because there is no path from, say, vertex 1 to vertex 8. Though that graph is not connected, it has—here I'm inserting a new definition—three different "connected components." You can see the three connected components in the graph, and yes, that single point consisting of vertex 8 is considered to be connected. It's its own connected component.

Next, we'll define a trail, which is a walk with no repeated edges. A path is a walk with no repeated vertices; a trail is a walk with no repeated edges. For example, the trail that goes from 1 to 5, 5 to 2, 2 to 3, 3 to 5 again, and 5 to 4, though that wouldn't be a path, because the vertex 5 was repeated, it is a trail because none of the edges were repeated. A trail is closed if it begins and ends at the same vertex. If I took that same trail, 1 to 5 to 2 to 3 to 5 to 4, and I insert one more step that goes from 4 to 1, that would be a closed trail. Here's another example of a closed trail in this graph G that goes from 5 to 2 to 3 to 5. That would be a special kind of closed trail, which we call a cycle. A cycle looks like a polygon, or it can be straightened out to look like a polygon.

Here's the official definition: A cycle of length k is a closed trail that goes v_0 to v_1, up until v_k—and since it's a closed trail, v_k has to be the same as v_0—with the property that until you took that last step, you had a path—that is, v_0, v_1 up through v_{k-1} is a path. Here are some examples of cycles; in fact, these are graphs that are themselves cycle graphs. Here's what we might call C_4, which looks like a square; C_5, which looks like a pentagon; or even this star graph is also a cycle. It doesn't look like a polygon, but it could be straightened out so that we would have a polygon.

Here's a new question for you: Can you draw this graph without lifting your pen off the paper, and you're not allowed to retrace any of the edges? This puzzle you might have seen as child. They give you this picture and say, draw this graph without lifting your pencil off the paper. Can you do it? Maybe I shouldn't spoil the fun for you, but the answer is yes, you can draw this graph if you're careful. Starting at vertex 3, you can go from 3 to 6, 6 to 5, 5 to 2, 2 to 6, then to 4, to 5, to 1, to 2, to 3, and then to 4. We call a graph like this "drawable."

Here's the official definition: A graph G is drawable if it's connected and G contains a trail that uses every edge exactly once. For example, is this graph drawable? [It's the] same graph without the little roof on top of it. You can try all you like, but the answer is no; this graph is not drawable. If you wanted to draw every edge in the graph, you would have to retrace an edge somehow. But how do we prove it? Here's the key observation to all proofs about drawable graphs: If G is drawable as a trail from x to y, then the graph G has to be connected, and every vertex, except maybe your starting and endpoints, x and y, must have even degree. I'll say that again: In a drawable graph, if you can draw it as a trail from x to y, everything has to have even degree, except maybe for the vertices x and y. Why is that?

Let's look at a vertex that's not x or y. Then every time the trail enters v with an edge, then it must exit v using a different edge. Since every time we enter a vertex, we have to leave it with a different edge, that proves that there must be an even number of edges that are attached to v. In other words, the degree of v must be even. Consequently, if my graph has any hope of being drawable, then it has to have at most two vertices of odd degree. Since the graph in our picture has the degree of 2 is 3, the degree of 3 is 3, the degree of 4 is 3, and the degree of 5 is 3—the degree of 6 is 4; that's fine—but I have four vertices of odd degree. Our last observation said, in order to be drawable, you must have at most two vertices of odd degree, so the above graph is not drawable.

Let's take a look at this graph. This was the graph we saw earlier. If we look at the degrees of the vertices here, we see that the degree of 1 is 2, the degree of 2 is 4, the degree of 3 is 3, the degree of 4 is 3, the degree of 5 is 4, and the degree of 6 is 4. Here we have two vertices of odd degree—vertices 3 and 4. Is it drawable? We knew it was drawable from before, but now what we know is that any trail that draws G would have to have endpoints 3 and 4, because we know everything other than the endpoints must have even degree. If you had trouble figuring out how to draw that graph before, it was because you were starting from the wrong point.

Can the graph that we just saw be drawn in such a way that it begins and ends at the same vertex? No, because if it begins and ends at the same vertex, that would mean, in particular, that it might have to begin and end at 3, or begin and end at 4, or begin and end anywhere else. That would require that every vertex have even degree. If you want to draw your graph as a closed trail, then every vertex has to have even degree.

Let's take a look; if we modify our graph by inserting a new vertex 7 and connecting vertices 3 and 4, now every vertex has even degree. Every vertex has even degree, including 3, including 4, including this new vertex 7. Can we draw the graph as a closed trail? Sure, we could start at 3 and do the same thing we did before, and end at 4, and then we take our two new edges, we go from 4 to 7 and 7 to 3, and we've drawn our graph this time as a closed trail. Or we could modify our graph by just adding an edge that goes from 3 to 4. We would no longer have a graph any more; technically, we would have a multigraph. Nevertheless, we would be able to draw it as a closed trail. Again, it would be drawable and begin and end where it started.

These kinds of graphs are called Eulerian. The official definition is that a graph or multigraph G is Eulerian if it's connected and G contains a closed trail that uses every edge. Every Eulerian graph is drawable, but not every drawable graph is Eulerian because to be Eulerian, not only do you have to be drawable, [but] you have to be drawable in such a way that you end at the same place that you started. For example, the first drawable graph that we saw, though that's drawable, it's not Eulerian because I can't begin and end at the same point, nor is this other graph.

Here's an important observation about Eulerian graphs. If a graph is Eulerian, you can start and end at any vertex. There's no special starting and ending point of an Eulerian graph; it's like a continuous piece of rope. For instance, to take a trivial Eulerian graph, this little square, this cycle, you could draw this as a, b, c, d, a, or you could start at b and go b, c, d, a, b, or c, d, a, b, c, and so on. There's no place that has to be a starting point. Any place can be a starting point in an Eulerian graph.

These graphs, by the way, are called Eulerian because Euler—whom we've met before—invented graph theory in 1736 to solve the following problem. This is known as the Bridges of Konigsberg problem. In the Prussian town of Konigsberg, now the Russian town of Kaliningrad, just north of Poland, the Pregel River flows through the town, which included an island and seven bridges, as illustrated. The question that they were interested in was: Is it possible to walk around the city, crossing each bridge exactly once, and if possible, return to their starting point? Euler invented the concepts of graph theory to solve this problem. By representing each vertex as a region and each bridge as an edge, we get the following multigraph. You can look at this multigraph, and since this multigraph clearly has four vertices of odd degree—the degree of a is 5, the degree of b is 3, the degree of c is 3, and the degree of d is 3—then [with] four vertices of odd degree, this graph is not drawable, and certainly, if it's not drawable, it's not Eulerian. Hence, there is no way to tour the city crossing each bridge once.

So far, we've shown that if G is an Eulerian graph or multigraph, then G must be connected and every vertex must have the even degree. But what about the converse? What is the converse? Is it true that if the graph is connected and every vertex has even degree, then must the graph be Eulerian? Must you then be able to draw the graph without retracing any edges and end up where you started? You might be surprised to know that the answer is yes. If a graph is connected and every vertex has even degree, then G is Eulerian.

We'll prove this theorem using strong induction. What are we inducting on here? We're going to induct on the number of edges. We begin by looking at a graph that's connected and every vertex has even degree, where the number of edges is 0; how many graphs are like that? Just one, a pretty boring graph; [it] looks like a single point. We've proved the theorem beyond a shadow of a doubt when the number of edges is 0. Now we state our strong induction hypothesis: Suppose the theorem is true for all graphs with fewer than E edges, and now, let G be a graph with E edges, and we have to show that it is Eulerian. We know the graph's connected; that means it doesn't have any vertices of degree 0. It doesn't have any of those isolated points because it wouldn't be connected then. Since every vertex has degree at least 2, then I claim that G must have a cycle. Why is that? If every vertex has degree at least 2, then you start at a vertex, you walk to a new vertex, and if you've only walked into it once, there has to be a place to go because it has degree 2. You walk to a new vertex, and a new vertex, and a new vertex; because there are only a finite number of vertices in our graph, then you have to eventually go back to a vertex that you were already at, and once you've done that, you will have created a cycle.

A graph where every vertex has even degree, at least 2, must have a cycle. Let's call such a cycle C. If C uses every edge of G, then congratulations; you've just drawn your graph G as one big cycle, and G would therefore be Eulerian, and we'd be done. Otherwise, if you're not so lucky, what do you do? Let's create the graph $G - C$. Let's remove the cycle from the graph, and look at what we get. For instance, take a look at this fishy graph here in this picture. It's a connected graph, every vertex has even degree—every vertex has degree 2 or 4—and in it, we must have a cycle. There's a cycle C. Let's remove the cycle C from our graph. When I'm removing that cycle, I'm leaving the vertices in place; I'm just getting rid of the edges. That gives me this new graph, $G - C$.

What happens when you remove a cycle from a graph? What happens to the degrees of the vertices? Every vertex in that cycle is going to lose two of its edges, so every vertex in the cycle, the degree goes down by 2. Every vertex that's not in the cycle, the degree doesn't change at all. Every vertex has its degree reduced by 0 or 2, reduced by an even number. Since the parity doesn't change, every vertex of $G - C$ still has even degree. If this graph $G - C$ is connected, like here in our picture, then by the induction hypothesis, $G - C$—since it has fewer edges than G did—has to be Eulerian. Hence, we can draw the graph G as a closed tour—the original graph G as a closed tour—by drawing C and then drawing $G - C$. If $G - C$ is not connected, then by the induction hypothesis, each of its connected components, which have fewer edges than the original graph did, is itself Eulerian. Since G is connected, each of these components of $G - C$ had to make contact with C somewhere. If they didn't, the original graph G wouldn't have been connected.

Here, we go around the cycle C, and any time we're at a new connected component, we tour that component. We draw that component before continuing on C as shown in our illustration. As an exercise, you might want to try the problem: If G is a connected graph or multigraph with exactly two vertices of odd degree—say, vertices x and y—then G can be drawn as a trail from x to y. Hint: Insert an edge from x to y and apply the previous theorem.

Now we present an application of Eulerian graphs that doesn't sound like a problem from graph theory. Here are the binary words of length 2: 00, 01, 11, and 10. Notice that the sequence 0011 includes every one of these code words exactly once as a consecutive pair. That is, 0011 starts off with 00; and then if I slide over, we have 01; then if I slide over, we have 11; and then if I slide over and wrap around, we have 10. We efficiently created all the code words in that sequence. Here are the binary words of length 3. We know there are eight of them, and all eight of those are contained in the sequence 00010111. Check it out for yourself, allowing yourself to wrap around. This includes every one of these code words exactly once as a consecutive triple, allowing wraparound. This allows us to efficiently list all eight code words in one sequence. Such a sequence is called a de Bruijn sequence. Whether I'm using 2 code words, 4 code words, 8, 16, 32; that's a de Bruijn sequence. The question is: Can a de Bruijn sequence be created for all of the 2^n binary words of length n? The answer is yes, and it's based on an Eulerian graph where every vertex represents a word of length $n - 1$, and every word has two edges entering it and two edges leaving it, like the one in the picture here.

Let me explain this graph here. This is a "directed graph," where every vertex has two edges leaving it and two edges entering it. I've got two vertices that have a loop that does double duty. We can use this graph here to create a de Bruijn sequence for all 16 code words of length 4. Notice I have 8 vertices here; each one represents a different triple. From the vertex *abc*, we have an edge that's labeled 0 that goes to the word *bc*0 and an edge labeled 1 that goes to the word *bc*1. It's like moving our slider over one space. [Thus,] *abc* is going to look like—after I move my slider—*bc*0 or *bc*1. Take a look at this graph. We see that every vertex has even in-degree and even out-degree. Therefore, by the same reasoning, this graph is Eulerian. When you draw the Eulerian circuit, that gives you the de Bruijn sequence.

Eulerian graphs, by the way, are sometimes confused with Hamiltonian graphs, which are entirely different objects. A graph is Hamiltonian if it contains a cycle that goes through every vertex. Whereas in an Eulerian graph, you could draw the whole graph and use up every edge, a Hamiltonian graph doesn't have to use every edge; it just has to go through every vertex. For example, this graph is not Eulerian—we've seen that before; it has four vertices of odd degree—but it is Hamiltonian since it contains this cycle. We can visit every vertex exactly once and get back to where we started. While there is a simple test to see if a graph is Eulerian—just check that it's connected and that the degree of each vertex is even— there's no simple test to see if a graph is Hamiltonian. We'll have more to say about this situation when we talk about algorithms and complexity in Lecture Twenty-Three.

In our next lecture, we combine graph theory with combinatorics using another fundamental tool of mathematics—matrices— where we'll answer the question: How do I walk to thee? Let me count the ways.

Lecture Seventeen
Ways to Walk—Matrices and Markov Chains

Scope:

Given a graph, it is natural to ask how many ways you can walk from one vertex to another. To answer this question, we introduce the idea of a matrix, which is essentially a box of numbers. Matrices can be added and subtracted in a natural way, but the rule for matrix multiplication is a little unusual, and matrix division is not always possible. Any graph can be represented by an adjacency matrix, where the (i, j) entry of the matrix is 1 if vertices i and j are adjacent and is 0 otherwise. We show that if a graph has adjacency matrix A, then the number of walks from vertex i to vertex j that use exactly N steps is simply the (i, j) entry of the matrix A^N. Now suppose that when you walk on a graph, when you are at vertex i, you walk to vertex j with probability p_{ij} This is called a Markov chain. Markov chains are used for modeling random processes.

Outline

I. Considering how a computer sees a graph, we use matrices to address the question "How many ways can you walk from one vertex to another in a given graph?"

   A. One way that a computer can represent a graph is by using an adjacency matrix, where the entry in the ith row and j^{th} column of the matrix is the number of edges that go from i to j.

   1. For example, the graph with edges $\{1, 2\}$, $\{1, 3\}$, $\{1, 4\}$, $\{2, 3\}$, and $\{3, 4\}$ has the adjacency matrix that follows.

$$\begin{bmatrix} 0 & 1 & 1 & 1 \\ 1 & 0 & 1 & 0 \\ 1 & 1 & 0 & 1 \\ 1 & 0 & 1 & 0 \end{bmatrix}$$

   2. Note that this definition works for graphs, multigraphs, and oriented graphs as well.

   B. Matrix addition is easy. You simply add the entries componentwise.

C. But matrix multiplication is trickier. When multiplying 2 square matrices, say $AB = C$, then C_{ij} (the entry of C in row i and column j) is the dot product of the ith row of A with the jth column of B. For example,

$$\begin{pmatrix} 1 & 2 \\ 3 & 4 \end{pmatrix}\begin{pmatrix} 5 & 6 \\ 7 & 8 \end{pmatrix} = \begin{pmatrix} 19 & 22 \\ 43 & 50 \end{pmatrix}$$

since $(1, 2)$ dotted with $(5, 7) = 5 + 14 = 19$; $(1, 2)$ dotted with $(6, 8) = 6 + 16 = 22$; and so on.

D. Using adjacency matrices, we have an elegant way to count walks in a graph. Theorem: Let G be a graph (or multigraph) with adjacency matrix A. Then the number of length-L walks from vertex i to vertex j is the (i, j) entry of A^L.

II. A random walk is a walk with distinct probabilities for each step.

A. Suppose you take random steps in your graph, so that when you are at vertex i, you move to vertex j with some probability p_{ij}.

B. For the graph considered earlier, if we move to adjacent vertices with equal probability, then we have the transition probability matrix P.

$$P = \begin{bmatrix} 0 & 1/3 & 1/3 & 1/3 \\ 1/2 & 0 & 1/2 & 0 \\ 1/3 & 1/3 & 0 & 1/3 \\ 1/2 & 0 & 1/2 & 0 \end{bmatrix}$$

C. Theorem: For a random walk on graph G with transition probability matrix P, when starting at vertex i, the probability that we are in state j in L steps is the (i, j) entry of P^L.

III. The process of randomly walking on a graph is called a Markov chain. Markov chains can be used to model any process where things move randomly from one state to another.

IV. The World Wide Web can be thought of as one giant directed graph.

A. Suppose there is a directed edge from webpage i to webpage j if there is a link from page i to page j.

B. Then if we wander the Web at random, we will spend more time at webpages that are popular than at webpages that are unpopular.

C. By calculating equilibrium probabilities in a certain way, a search engine can measure a webpage's importance. This idea is exploited by many efficient search engines.

D. Similar applications of Markov chains can be found that model population dynamics, genetics, stock prices, and games like blackjack.

E. In each of these situations, your prediction of where you will be at the next moment in time is based on where you are now.

Suggested Reading:

Bogart, *Introductory Combinatorics*, chap. 4.

Chartrand, *Introductory Graph Theory*, chap. 10.

Rosen, *Discrete Mathematics and Its Applications*, chap. 8.

Questions to Consider:

1. Determine the adjacency matrix for the graph below.

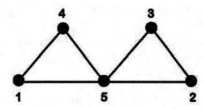

2. Use this adjacency matrix to determine the number of walks from vertex 1 to vertex 5 that take exactly 4 steps.

3. Draw the graph that has adjacency matrix $A = \begin{pmatrix} 0 & 1 & 0 & 0 \\ 1 & 0 & 1 & 1 \\ 1 & 1 & 0 & 1 \\ 1 & 1 & 1 & 0 \end{pmatrix}$.

4. Suppose that a sunny day has a 50% chance of being followed by a sunny day, and a cloudy day has a 75% chance of being followed by a cloudy day.

   a. Create the 2 × 2 transition probability matrix for this problem.

   b. Given that today is sunny, what is the probability that it will be cloudy 2 days from now?

   c. In the long run, what fraction of days are sunny?

Lecture Seventeen—Transcript
Ways to Walk—Matrices and Markov Chains

In our last lecture, we talked about various different kinds of walks on a graph—paths, trails, Eulerian tours, and so on. In this lecture, instead of describing new types of walks, we address a combinatorial question that involves counting walks. How many ways can you walk from one vertex to another? This will lead to a discussion of random walks on graphs and basic concepts of how many search engines rank Web pages.

Before turning to the World Wide Web, we begin with a much smaller example. In this graph, how many walks are there from vertex 1 to vertex 3 that have a given length L? For instance, if L is 1, I'm asking, how many walks are there from vertex 1 to vertex 3 of length 1? You can see in the graph, there's just 1 walk that goes from 1 to 3. How about when L is 2? How many walks of length 2? You can either get there by going 1 to 2 to 3, or you could go 1, 4, 3; there are 2 walks. How about, how many walks of length 3? There are 5 walks; you can go 1, 2, 1, 3; or 1, 3, 1, 3; or 1, 4, 1, 3; or 1, 3, 2, 3; or 1, 3, 4, 3. I won't count them all out, but there are 14 walks of length 4, 33 walks of length 5, 90 walks of length 6, and so on. The question is, how would we or a computer determine these numbers?

First, a more fundamental question: Before a computer can count walks in a graph, how does a computer actually see a graph? How does it represent it? There are a few ways of doing it. One is just by using the definition of a graph. It says, I know the vertex set is 1, 2, 3, 4; I know the edge set consists of these five edges, and that's enough to represent the graph. Or it might represent it as a list. It might say, vertex 1 is adjacent to vertices 2, 3, and 4; and vertex 2 is adjacent to 1 and 3; vertex 3 is adjacent to 1, 2 and 4; vertex 4 is adjacent to 1 and 3. That would be another way that the computer could represent the graph. But another way of representing the graph, the one that we're going to focus on in this lecture, is using something called an "adjacency matrix." The computer could represent the graph using this adjacency matrix. "What is this?" I hear you cry. Let's get acquainted with some basic properties of matrices and all will be made clear.

What's a matrix? Essentially, you can think of a matrix as a box of numbers. Here's a typical matrix, you might call it the π matrix because it has the digits 3, 1, 4, 1, 5, 9. This matrix, which I'll call A, has two rows and three columns, so we call it a two-by-three matrix—two rows, three columns. We say that the element $a_{i,j}$ refers to the number that's in row i and column j. Here, $a_{1,3}$ is 4, because the number 4 appears in row 1, column 3. Or we can say that the (1, 3) entry of the matrix A is 4.

The adjacency matrix for our graph is defined as follows: It consists of 0s and 1s, where we put a 1 in the (i, j) position if vertex i is adjacent to vertex j; otherwise, we put a 0. Another way of defining it equivalently is that $a_{i,j}$ is simply the number of edges that go between i and j, and in a graph, the number of edges between i and j is either going to be 1, if they're adjacent, or 0, if they're not adjacent. For instance, if you look at our graph here, you see that vertex 1 is adjacent to vertices 2, 3, and 4, and that's why row 1 has a 1 in columns 2, 3, and 4, and it has a 0 in the 1, 1 position, because the vertex is not considered to be adjacent to itself because it doesn't have an edge that goes back to itself. [Note that] vertex 2 is only adjacent to vertices 1 and 3; that's why we have a 1 in the first column and the third column of row 2 and the rest are 0s. Check to make sure that you see that this matrix represents this graph.

Adjacency matrices can also represent multigraphs using that same definition of $a_{i,j}$ being the number of edges that connect vertex i and vertex j. We see that this multigraph would have this adjacency matrix. For example, you see we have two edges that connect vertex 1 and vertex 2, and that's why the 1, 2 entry is 2. We also have a loop that goes from 4 back to 4, and that's why the 4, 4 entry is 1. Again, verify that this multigraph has this adjacency matrix. Adjacency matrices can also represent directed graphs. Those are graphs where each edge is given an orientation, kind of like one-way streets. For example, here we have an edge that goes from 1 to 2, and we'll let $a_{i,j}$ be the number of edges that go from i to j. For instance, the entry of $a_{1,2}$, that would be 1, whereas $a_{2,1}$ is 0; there is no edge that goes from 2 back to 1.

By the way, I should point out that with graphs and multigraphs, if there is no orientation of the edges, then your graph is symmetric. That means the number of edges that go from i to j is the same as the number of edges that go from j to i. That means [that] your adjacency matrix is going to have the same number in the ij position as it will in the ji position. But, with a directed graph, you're generally not going to be symmetric. Like here, $a_{1,2}$ is 1, but $a_{2,1}$ is 0.

Using adjacency matrices, we can calculate the number of walks of any length for a graph, or multigraph, or directed graph; all we need to be able to do is to multiply matrices. Let me tell you all you need to know about matrix arithmetic for this lecture. First of all, matrix addition is easy; you add them just as you'd expect to add them. For instance, here's the matrix $\begin{bmatrix} 1 & 2 \\ 3 & 4 \end{bmatrix}$ + the matrix $\begin{bmatrix} 5 & 6 \\ 7 & 8 \end{bmatrix}$. When you add them—how would you want to add them? Component-wise—$1 + 5$ is 6; $2 + 6$ is 8; $3 + 7$ is 10; $4 + 8$ is 12, and that would be correct. Matrix addition [is] a piece of cake; matrix multiplication [is] a little trickier. In fact, let me tell you right off the bat, $\begin{bmatrix} 1 & 2 \\ 3 & 4 \end{bmatrix} \times \begin{bmatrix} 5 & 6 \\ 7 & 8 \end{bmatrix}$ does not equal $\begin{bmatrix} 5 & 12 \\ 21 & 32 \end{bmatrix}$. We don't multiply components together.

How do we multiply matrices? [We do it] using something called a "dot product." Let me explain it through this example: I'm going to take the 2-by-2 matrix $\begin{bmatrix} 1 & 2 \\ 3 & 4 \end{bmatrix}$ × the 2-by-2 matrix $\begin{bmatrix} 5 & 6 \\ 7 & 8 \end{bmatrix}$. That is going to create a 2-by-2 matrix. Let's first calculate the number that's in the first row and the first column. I do that using the first row of the first matrix times the first column of the second matrix. When I say "times," I really mean using something called the "dot product," and here's how it goes: To do the row 1, 2 dotted with the column 5, 7, I take $(1 \times 5) + (2 \times 7)$—that's $5 + 14$, giving me 19.

Let's do a few more examples. To get the $(1, 2)$ entry of the product, I'm going to take row 1 from the first matrix and dot it with column 2 of the second matrix, and when I take 1, 2 dotted with 6, 8, I get $6 + 16$, which is 22. To get the next entry, to get the $(2, 1)$, entry of the product, this time I'm going to take row 2 of the first matrix dotted with column 1 of the second matrix, giving us 43, in this case. Finally, for the last entry, for $(2, 2)$, entry, I'll take the second row of the first matrix dotted with the second column of the second matrix, giving me 50.

In general, if A and B are an n-by-n matrices, then their product, $A \times B$, is also an n-by-n matrix. The number that you get in row i and column j is obtained by taking the ith row of A and dotting it with the jth column of B. One important word of caution; if there's anything you remember about matrix multiplication it should be this: Matrix multiplication is not usually commutative. That is, $A \times B$ is generally not equal to $B \times A$. As this example shows you, $\begin{bmatrix} 1 & 2 \\ 3 & 4 \end{bmatrix} \times \begin{bmatrix} 5 & 6 \\ 7 & 8 \end{bmatrix}$ does not give you the same matrix as $\begin{bmatrix} 5 & 6 \\ 7 & 8 \end{bmatrix} \times \begin{bmatrix} 1 & 2 \\ 3 & 4 \end{bmatrix}$. But matrix multiplication is associative. What associative means is: You don't have to worry about parentheses. That is, $A(BC)$ is the same as $(AB)C$. I haven't changed the orders of the matrices A, B, and C; I just changed how I parenthesized things. I won't prove to you that matrix multiplication is associative, but that's definitely worth knowing. For example, A^3, you can think of that as $A \times A \times A$, which is either $A \times A^2$ or $A^2 \times A$. You can calculate A^3 either way.

Because matrix multiplication is defined this way, we can solve our original combinatorial question, the question of how many length-L walks exist from vertex i to vertex j, very easily. Here's the theorem: Let G be a graph, or a multigraph, or a directed graph with adjacency matrix A. Then, the number of length-L walks from vertex i to vertex j is simply the (i, j) entry of the matrix A^L power. Let me say that again. In other words, to find the number of length-L walks from i to j, you take the matrix A, raise it to the Lth power, then look at the number that appears in the ith row and j^{th} column, and that's your answer.

Let's do some examples with the original matrix that we had. Here's our graph G and there's its adjacency matrix A. How many length-1 walks are there from 1 to 3? We just look at the $(1, 3)$ entry of A, and there it is. We knew it would be there; that was part of the definition. How about the number of length-2 walks? We know there are 2 walks of length 2; let's see if the matrix can find it. We take the matrix A^2, so we take $A \times A$. We calculate A^2, and we look at the $(1, 3)$ entry of our matrix, and we see that the $(1, 3)$ entry of our matrix A^2 is 2, so the theorem says there are 2 walks of length 2 from 1 to 3.

How many walks of length 3? That's going to be the $(1, 3)$ entry of the matrix A^3. I can get that by taking the first row of A times the third column of A^2 because A^3 is $A \times A^2$. When I do that dot product, I get 5 as the $(1, 3)$ entry of A^3, and therefore, there are 5 walks of length 3 from 1 to 3. How many walks of length 4? This will be the

(1, 3) entry of A^4. Now, A^4, that's $A^2 \times A^2$. I could take row 1 of A^2 dotted with column 3 of A^2, and when I do that dot product, I get 14, as promised.

This theorem can be proved by induction on L, and I'll sketch it for you here. When $L = 1$, the theorem is true by the definition of the adjacency matrix A. After all, a_{ij} is the number of length-1 walks from i to j—it's the number of edges from i to j. To prove this inductively, our induction hypothesis is: Assume that for every i and j, the number of length-k walks from i to j is the (i, j) entry of A^k. The question is: How many walks from i to j are there of length $k + 1$? I'm going to do that by first considering where the first step goes as I go from i to j. Let's say: How many of them go from i to the vertex m and then continue on to j? Such a walk is going to look like this: I take 1 step from i to m and then a k-step walk from m to j. How many ways can that be done? I know the number of length-1 walks from i to m is just the (i, m) entry of the matrix A. How many length-k walks are there from m to j? By the induction hypothesis, that's the (m, j) entry of A^k. When I sum over all values of m, this gives us the (i, j) entry of $A \times A^k$, which is equal to A^{k+1}.

Suppose you take random steps in your graph, so that when you're at vertex i, you move to vertex j with some probability p_{ij}. I want to talk about the subject of random walks now. For example, if we move in our original graph to adjacent vertices with equal probability—what I mean by equal probability is: If you're at vertex 1, you could go to 2, or 3, or 4, each with probability 1/3. But if you're at vertex 2, you can't go to vertex 4, but you can to go to vertex 1 or 3 with equal probability 1/2. We represent this with our "transition probability matrix." Here's the transition probability matrix P—sometimes I'll just call that the P matrix—for this graph. The (i, j) entry of our P matrix is the probability that we go from i to j when we're at vertex i.

Question: Given that we start in state 1, I'm asking, what's the probability that L moves from now we are in state 3? For example, let's start simple: When L is 1, what's the probability of going from vertex 1 to vertex 3 in one move? If you start at vertex 1, there's a 1 in 3 chance that you end up at vertex 3 on your next move, and that happens to be the $(1, 3)$ entry of our P matrix. When L is equal to 2, what's the probability that if we start at vertex 1, we end up at vertex 3 in 2 moves? There are two ways of getting to vertex 3, as we saw before; you can either go 1, 2, 3 or 1, 4, 3. The probability of taking walk 1, 2, 3 is $1/3 \times 1/2$, which is $1/6$. The reason for that is once you're at vertex 1, you have a $1/3$ chance of moving to vertex 2, and from vertex 2, you have a $1/2$ chance of going to 3. On the other hand, the walk 1, 4, 3, that also has a probability of $1/6$, because there's a 1 in 3 chance of going from 1 to 4, and a 1 in 2 chance of going from 4 to 3. Therefore, the total probability is $1/6 + 1/6$, which equals $1/3$.

For walks of length 3, there are 5 walks. I won't go through all of them, but their probabilities range from $1/18$ to $1/27$; let's just look at two of them. For example, the walk 1, 2, 1, 3, what's the probability of taking that? It's the probability of going from 1 to 2, then from 2 to 1, then from 1 to 3. When we multiply those probabilities, we have $1/3 \times 1/2 \times 1/3$, and that's equal to $1/18$. On the other hand, the walk 1, 3, back to 1, back to 3, that's going to have probability $1/3 \times 1/3 \times 1/3$, which is $1/27$. Adding up all those probabilities gives us a total of $7/27$ as the probability of going from 1 to 3 in three moves.

By essentially the same reason as in the last theorem, we have the following theorem: For a random walk on graph G, with probability matrix P, when starting at vertex i, the probability that we're in state j in L steps is the (i, j) entry of P^L power. This process of randomly walking on a graph is called a "Markov chain." Markov chains can be used to model any random process where things move randomly from one state to another [and] where the probability of moving from i to j only depends on your current state i and not where you were previously.

For instance, here's a rather simplified model of weather prediction. Let's imagine we consider there to be two states of weather; it's either sunny or cloudy. You're the weatherman, and you've decided that if it's sunny today, then there's an 80% chance that it will be sunny tomorrow and, therefore, a 20% chance that it will be cloudy tomorrow. On the other hand, if it's cloudy today, then there's a 60% chance that it will be cloudy tomorrow and, therefore, a 40% chance that it will be sunny tomorrow. We represent that by our P matrix in front of us, $\begin{bmatrix} .8 & .2 \\ .4 & .6 \end{bmatrix}$, representing the probability of going from a sunny or cloudy day to another sunny or cloudy day the next day. If that's the matrix P, if we want to predict the weather two days from now, we look at the matrix P^2. We know how to multiply matrices; we multiply $P \times P$, we get P^2. For P^3, we can take $P \times P^2$, multiply those together, and [that] gives us the matrix P^3. Let's take a look at that matrix P^3. It says, if it's sunny today, then the chance that it's cloudy in three days is going to be this entry, .312. That means that if it's sunny today, there's a 31.2% chance that it will be cloudy in three days.

Here are the matrices P^4, P^5, P^6, and P^7. Take a look at those entries; do you see anything interesting about them? Even though these are representing a random process, these numbers aren't looking very random, are they? Look at the last number, P^7; that first column, the numbers are like .667 and another number that's like .666. In the second column, the numbers—one of them is like .333; the other is like .334. It appears that as L gets larger and larger, P^L power is getting closer and closer to the first column, looking like 2/3, 2/3, and the second column, looking like 1/3, 1/3. What that says is that if you look far into the future, the chance of being sunny, under this weather model, is 66.7% regardless of whether today is sunny or cloudy.

This kind of makes sense. By the way, if you take a look at what would happen to the matrix $\begin{bmatrix} 2/3 & 1/3 \\ 2/3 & 1/3 \end{bmatrix}$—if you think of that as like P raised to the infinity power—look at what happens if you hit it with one more application of our P matrix. When you multiply .8, .2, .6, .4 times the matrix $\begin{bmatrix} 2/3 & 1/3 \\ 2/3 & 1/3 \end{bmatrix}$—do the math—you'll see you still get $\begin{bmatrix} 2/3 & 1/3 \\ 2/3 & 1/3 \end{bmatrix}$. This makes sense, since our equilibrium matrix doesn't change when we multiply it by P. Looking into the future infinity days from now is going to look just like looking into the future infinity + 1 day from now. This relationship allows us to find the equilibrium matrix without actually having to raise P to a large power. All you have to do is solve a system of equations.

Incidentally, suppose you had a more accurate model that predicted tomorrow's weather based on the weather today and yesterday. Could you model that with a Markov chain? Remember, Markov chains are only supposed to be based on what's going on now. The answer is you actually could, but instead of it being a 2-by-2 matrix modeling the situation, it would be a 4-by-4 matrix, and it would have this kind of structure. We would have four states, not just two, representing sunny or cloudy, but all possibilities for the last two days. We have *SS*, *CS*, *CC*, and *SC*; a state like *SC* on the bottom would mean that it was sunny yesterday and cloudy today.

Let's go to the top row and look at what happens. If it was sunny yesterday and sunny today, then what's the possible situation for the next day? The next day it's either going to be sunny or cloudy. If it's sunny, we'll still be in the *SS* situation, but if the next day is cloudy, that's going to put us in an *SC* situation, because the next day's going to be cloudy, [but] the day before it—where we are now—is sunny. That puts us in an *SC* situation. But there's no way of going from an *SS* situation to a *CC* situation in one day, and there's no way even of getting from an *SS* situation to a *CS* situation in one day. That's the structure of these matrices. Obviously, the more days you want to be based on, the more complicated [it is], the more states are going to be required in your adjacency matrix.

By the way, if we think of the World Wide Web as one giant graph—it's a directed graph with an edge directed from Web page *i* to Web page *j*—if there's a Web link from page *i* to page *j*, then if we wander the Web at random, just like we were doing in our earlier example, then we're going to spend more time at Web pages that are popular than Web pages that are unpopular. By calculating equilibrium probabilities in a certain way, a search engine can measure a Web page's importance. When I say, "in a certain way," the main difference from the usual equilibrium calculation is that when it reaches a Web page with no escaping links, it moves to another Web page just anywhere in the world, entirely at random. This is one of the key components behind the page rank algorithm used by Google and other search engines.

Similar applications of Markov chains can be found at model population dynamics, genetics, stock prices, and games people play, like blackjack. In each of these situations, your prediction of where you'll be in the next moment in time is based on where you are now. For instance, if you're playing blackjack and you see that the dealer right now has a 6 showing, then your prediction on what he's going to have in the end is going to take advantage of the fact that he has a 6 showing now. Then when he gets another card—let's say a 4; then he's got a 10—that's going to revise your prediction of what his total is going to be at the end.

Speaking of games people play, stick around for our next lecture when we apply graph theory to the topic of social networks.

Lecture Eighteen
Social Networks and Stable Marriages

Scope:

One of the first theorems in graph theory is sometimes called the handshake theorem, which says that when a group of people meet and some of them shake hands, the total number of handshakes will always be even. In graph theoretic terms, it says that the sum of the degrees of all the vertices is equal to twice the number of edges. As an application, we extend our earlier result that among any 6 people, there must always exist 3 mutual friends or 3 mutual strangers. Building on that result and "armed" with the handshake theorem, we show that with 9 people, there must always be 3 mutual friends or 4 mutual strangers. We also discuss the stable marriage theorem, which shows that in a community with n men and n women who wish to be paired up for matrimony, there is always a way to do this in such a way that no extramarital affairs will take place.

Outline

I. Since a graph is a collection of vertices and edges, where the vertices are connected by an edge if they are related in some way, then it is not surprising that graph theory has been used to model social activities.

A. The handshake theorem says that the sum of the degrees of the vertices of a graph must be twice the number of edges.

B. The proof is that if we count the edges that leave each vertex, then every edge is counted exactly twice.

C. The following set of graphs will play an important role: A complete graph K_n consists of n vertices, where every pair of vertices is adjacent. For example, K_3 looks like a triangle and K_4 would look like a square with both diagonals included.

II. Complete graphs give us insight into the number of mutual friends and strangers using Ramsey's theorem.

   A. Ramsey's (3, 3) theorem says that among any 6 people, there must exist 3 mutual friends or 3 mutual strangers. This was stated and proved in Lecture One. But we can say it another way in terms of complete graphs. If every edge of K_6 is colored red (friend) or blue (stranger), then there must exist a red K_3 or a blue K_3.

   B. Ramsey's (3, 4) theorem says that any group of 10 people must contain 3 mutual friends or 4 mutual strangers. Equivalently, if every edge of K_{10} is colored red or blue, then it must have a red K_3 or a blue K_4.

   C. In fact, Ramsey's (3, 4) theorem can be strengthened to 9 people: If every edge of K_9 is colored red or blue, then it must have a red K_3 or a blue K_4.

III. The stable marriage problem is another classic application of discrete mathematics to social networks.

   A. Suppose that you have been hired to be the matchmaker for a town with n men and n women who wish to be paired up with each other in a logical way. Each man provides you with a list of the names of all n women, ranked from first choice to last choice, and the women similarly provide you with a list ranking all n men.

   B. Your job is to provide a way to pair up the n men and n women in such a way that no extramarital affairs will take place. In other words, there is no man i and no woman j so that i and j prefer each other over the mates they have been assigned.

   C. The stable marriage theorem says that your job can always be accomplished, no matter how the men and women have ranked each other. Better still, it provides an algorithm that accomplishes your task.

D. In round 1, every man proposes to his first choice. Those women who receive offers tentatively accept the best offer and tell the other men not to come back. The rejected men then propose to their next choice, and the women again tentatively accept the best offer they have so far received and tell the other proposers to go away. This process continues until eventually every woman has tentatively accepted someone (at which point there are no rejected men), and the matchmaker assigns the men to the women in this way.

E. This assignment is guaranteed to be stable. Why? Suppose man i is more interested in woman j than the woman he was assigned. But then he would have already proposed to woman j, and she rejected him for someone else, whom she preferred. Therefore, although man i is interested in woman j, woman j is not interested in man i.

F. A version of this algorithm is actually used to match medical residents with hospitals.

IV. Mathematicians have playfully created a collaboration graph in honor of Paul Erdös, who wrote more than 1400 mathematical papers (more than any other mathematician) and had more than 500 collaborators.

A. A person's Erdös number is the number of steps that it takes to get to the vertex represented by Erdös.

B. Erdös himself has an Erdös number of 0. Anyone who has written a paper with Erdös has an Erdös number of 1.

C. Anyone who has written a paper with someone who has written a paper with Erdös has Erdös number 2, and so on.

Suggested Reading:

Chartrand, *Introductory Graph Theory*, secs. 5, 8.

Rosen, *Discrete Mathematics and Its Applications*, chap. 4.

West, *Introduction to Graph Theory*, chap. 8.

Questions to Consider:

1. Find a graph with vertex set $V = \{1, 2, 3, 4, 5\}$ and the given degree sequence, or explain why such a graph cannot exist.

   a. $d(1) = 1$, $d(2) = 1$, $d(3) = 2$, $d(4) = 2$, $d(5) = 2$.

   b. $d(1) = 2$, $d(2) = 2$, $d(3) = 2$, $d(4) = 2$, $d(5) = 4$.

   c. $d(1) = 0$, $d(2) = 1$, $d(3) = 2$, $d(4) = 3$, $d(5) = 4$.

   d. $d(1) = 0$, $d(2) = 1$, $d(3) = 2$, $d(4) = 3$, $d(5) = 3$.

2. Prove that among 18 people, there must be 4 mutual friends or 4 mutual strangers. (Hint: You may use the fact that with 9 people, there must be 4 mutual friends or 3 mutual strangers.)

3. In the stable marriage problem with n men and n women, how many different lists could the matchmaker receive? (Hint: When $n = 1, 2$, and 3, the answers are 1, 4, and 36, respectively.)

4. Suppose the matchmaker receives the following lists:

   Man 1: (3, 1, 4, 2, 5; i.e., his first choice is woman 3, followed by woman 1, and so on); man 2: (1, 3, 5, 2, 4); man 3: (5, 4, 3, 2, 1); man 4: (1, 5, 4, 2, 3); man 5: (3, 4, 5, 1, 2); woman 1: (3, 5, 1, 4, 2); woman 2: (3, 1, 2, 4, 5); woman 3: (1, 2, 3, 4, 5); woman 4: (5, 3, 1, 2, 4); woman 5: (5, 4, 2, 3, 1).

   a. Use the stable marriage algorithm to find a stable pairing.

   b. Find another stable pairing obtained by having the women propose to the men.

5. **a.** How many perfect matchings are in the wheel graph W_6 below, consisting of 6 vertices—a cycle of 5 vertices, along with a sixth vertex that is adjacent to everything on the cycle?

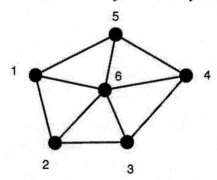

   b. How many perfect matchings are in the wheel graph W_n?

Lecture Eighteen—Transcript
Social Networks and Stable Marriages

Since a graph is a collection of vertices and edges, where the vertices are connected by an edge if they are related in some way, then it's not surprising that graph theory's been used to model social activities which arise as the result of human interaction. In fact, in many graph theory courses, the first theorem presented often goes by the name of the "handshake theorem." Recall, in a graph, the degree of a vertex, denoted d of v, is the number of vertices adjacent to v or, equivalently, the number of edges that use vertex v. For example in this graph, the degree of vertex 5 (d of 5) is 4. The handshake theorem goes like this; it says simply: The sum of the degrees of the vertices is twice the number of edges. Repeat that with me: The sum of the degrees of the vertices is twice the number of edges. This can be expressed algebraically as follows: Suppose a graph has n vertices—v_1, v_2, through v_n—and it has e edges, then the $d(v_1) + d(v_2)$ up to $d(v_n)$ is always equal to twice e, twice the number of edges.

Let's verify that for the graph we have in front of us. Here, e is 7—we have 7 edges—and the degrees of vertices 1 through 8 are, respectively, 2, 2, 2, 2, 4, 1, 1, and 0. Adding those numbers together we get 14, which is twice 7, that is, twice the number of edges. The proof is pretty simple. If we count the edges that leave each vertex, then every edge is counted exactly twice. This is called the handshake theorem since if at a party, everyone keeps track of the number of people whose hands they shook, then the sum of the numbers must be even. Here, every vertex represents a person and every edge represents two handshakes—x shaking the hand of y, and y shaking the hand of x.

New definition: A complete graph K_n—think of K as standing for "complete." It doesn't really mean complete; I'll tell you what it stands for later. Anyway, K_n consists of n vertices where every pair of vertices is adjacent. That's why it's complete; every possible edge that could be there is there. For instance, here's K_1 with just 1 point. Here is K_2 with 2 vertices connected by an edge. K_3 looks like a triangle. K_4—that's not a square, but rather, it's this configuration—it has 6 edges, all possible connections are being made. Or if you'd rather not draw it as a square with an X in it, you could draw it this way, looking a little like a tetrahedron, if you will.

Sometimes we don't label the vertices of the graph. It's OK to write K_5 looking simply like that. In our very first lecture, we encountered Ramsey's theorem. I'm going to present to you the (3, 3) version of Ramsey's theorem. It says: Among any 6 people, there must always be 3 mutual friends or 3 mutual strangers. Or in the language of graph theory, if every edge of K_6 is colored red, where a red edge represents a friend, or colored blue, where a blue edge represents a stranger, then there must exist a red K_3 or a blue K_3. Again, every edge is colored either red or blue, and you can't avoid creating an all-red triangle or an all-blue triangle.

I'll run through the proof quickly. Vertex 6 must have either at least 3 red edges or at least 3 blue edges because it's got 5 edges leaving it. We'll assume, without loss of generality, it has at least 3 red edges leaving it. Let's say it has red edges going to a, b, and c. Now if any edge between a, b, or v is red, then that gives us a red triangle, a red K_3. On the other hand, if none of those edges [is] red, then we must have all of those edges being blue, giving us a blue triangle, a blue K_3. Either way, we find ourselves with a red K_3 or a blue K_3.

You might ask the question: Is the theorem true with 5 people? Must any group of 5 people contain 3 mutual friends or 3 mutual strangers? The answer is no, you don't necessarily have that situation. For example, suppose my graph K_5 was colored this way, with these 5 red edges and these 5 blue edges. Then, obviously, there's no red triangle—there's no red K_3—and, obviously, there's no blue triangle, no blue K_3—that's just a twisted pentagon if you look at it.

Now let's go to a new level. Let's look at what's called Ramsey's (3, 4) theorem, which says this: Any group of 10 people must contain 3 mutual friends or 4 mutual strangers—that's why it's the (3, 4) version. Any group of 10 people must contain 3 mutual friends or 4 mutual strangers, or equivalently, if every edge of K_{10} is colored red or blue, then it must contain a red K_3 or a blue K_4. Here's the proof: Consider vertex 10. It's true that since vertex 10 has 9 edges leaving it, then it must have either at least 5 red edges or at least 5 blue edges. That's true, but we need to work harder to get the blue K_4. Instead, I'm going to make another true statement, that is: Vertex 10, I claim, must have either at least 4 red edges leaving it or at least 6 blue edges leaving it. Why is that? Otherwise, it would have at most

3 red edges, at most 5 blue edges. That's at most 8 edges leaving it, and we know that vertex 10 has 9 edges leaving it.

I'm going to break this into two cases, and they both have to be considered separately. Case A: Suppose vertex 10 has at least 4 red edges leaving it. Let's say vertex 10 has a red edge going to a, b, c, and d. If any edges among a, b, c, and d are red, then that's going to give me a red triangle, a red K_3. If I have a red edge between a and b, then ab_{10} forms a red K_3.

On the other hand, if none of those edges are red, then they all have to be blue, but then that gives me a blue K_4. Do you see how that goes? We're not done though; that's just case A. That was the case where vertex 10 had at least 4 red edges. Now consider case B, where vertex 10 has at least 6 blue edges. Since it has at least 6 blue edges—that number 6 should sound familiar, right? We know that among 6 people, there must be 3 mutual friends or 3 mutual strangers. That is to say, among these 6 vertices, a through f, there must either be a red K_3 or a blue K_3. When I look at all the edges connecting them, they're all red or blue; there has to be, by Ramsey's (3, 3) theorem, a red K_3 or a blue K_3. If they have a red K_3, then we're done. Right here, we're done: bde, that forms a red K_3. Otherwise, we have a blue K_3. Here, if bde forms a blue K_3, then when you bring in vertex 10, we have a blue K_4. All of those vertices—b, d, e, and 10—are connected with blue edges. Either way, in case B, we're going to have a red K_3 or a blue K_4. [And] since it worked for case A and it worked for case B, then we're done.

You may ask the question: Is the theorem true with 9 vertices? Go ahead—ask the question. Is the theorem true with 9 vertices? The answer is yes and here's the proof: Consider K_9—no, not that K_9, the other K_9, the graph K_9, thank you. In the graph K_9, if every edge of K_9 is colored red or blue, then it must have a red K_3 or a blue K_4. I'm going to build on the previous proof. We know from the last proof, if any vertex—not just vertex 9—but if any vertex in the graph has 4 red edges or 6 blue edges, then we're done. Thus, we only have to consider the situation where every vertex 1 through 9 has exactly 3 red edges and exactly 5 blue edges. That means every vertex, with its 8 edges leaving it, 3 of them are red, and 5 of them are blue, because if you have 4 or more red edges, we're done. If you have 6 or more blue edges, we're done.

I claim this situation of everything having 3 red edges and 5 blue edges is actually impossible in K_9, since if we throw away the blue edges, what would we have left? We'd have a graph with 9 vertices where each vertex has degree 3. But then, the degree of vertex 1 + the degree of vertex 2 up through the degree of vertex 9 would be 27. But that's odd; literally, that's an odd number, and that's impossible. By the handshake theorem, we know the sum of the degrees of the vertices must be an even number, twice the number of edges. It can't be 27 because I know I don't have 13 ½ edges. You may ask the question: Is the theorem true with 8 vertices? Here the answer is no. That is, it's possible with 8 people to not have 3 mutual friends or 4 mutual strangers. For extra credit, try to find a way to color K_8 so that it has no red K_3 or blue K_4. It can be done with 12 red edges and 16 blue edges.

Ramsey's theorem goes beyond (3, 3) and (3, 4). The more general version says: For any numbers R and B, there is a number n so that if the edges of K_n are all colored red or blue, then it must contain either a red K_R or a blue K_B. This theorem, by the way, can be extended even with three or more colors. In fact, some people like to look at these things called Ramsey numbers; it's the smallest number that will make the red K_R or blue K_B theorem true. We've shown that the Ramsey number R(3, 3) is 6, and we've claimed that R(3, 4) is 9. It turns out R(4, 4) is 18. Once you get beyond that, a lot of the numbers we don't know exactly; we just know ranges of them. For instance, we know that the fifth Ramsey number, R(5, 5), must between 43 and 49. That is, with 49 or more, you definitely are going to have a red K_5 or a blue K_5 if you're coloring a graph with 49 or more vertices, and with 42 or fewer, you might not have a red K_5 or a blue K_5.

We know that the sixth Ramsey number lives somewhere between 102 and 165; that's a pretty big range. The great mathematician Paul Erdös asks us to imagine that aliens landed on Earth and demanded the value of R(5, 5), the fifth Ramsey number, or they would destroy our planet. In that case, he claims we should marshal all our computers and all our mathematicians and attempt to find the value. But suppose, instead, that they ask for the sixth Ramsey number; in that case, he believes we should gather all our resources to attempt to destroy the aliens.

Here's another classic application of discrete mathematics to social networks. Although it doesn't involve much graph theory, it's a problem that can be described and solved using discrete mathematical reasoning. It's called the stable marriage problem, and it goes like this: Suppose you've been hired to be the village matchmaker for a town with n men and n women who wish to be paired up with each other in a nice and logical way. Each man provides you with a list of the names of all n women, ranked from first choice to last choice. Every man has his own list; every man has his own preferences. Each woman does the same. She provides you with a list ranking all n men. Your job is to provide a way to pair up the n men and n women in such a way that no extramarital affairs will take place. In other words, there has to be no man i and no woman j so that i and j prefer each other over the mates they've been assigned. You have to pair them up in such a way that no hanky panky is going to happen. The stable marriage theorem says that your job can always be accomplished. No matter how the men and women have ranked each other, you can always find a stable pairing. Better still, it actually provides an algorithm that accomplishes your task.

Here's how it goes: In round 1, each man proposes to his first choice. Every man gets down on his knee and proposes to his top choice. Each woman that gets a proposal tentatively accepts her first choice and flat out rejects any other offer she got. The offer that sounded best to her, according to her preference list, she says, "I'll think it over with you, maybe—I'll give you a definite maybe," and to every other guy that proposed to her, she says, "No, I can do better than you; go away and never come back." Next, all the rejected men, what do they do? They now propose to their second choice, and the women behave again in the same sort of way. If a woman gets a better offer than the one that she's tentatively accepted, she'll tell the one that she's tentatively accepted to go away, she'll tentatively accept the new best offer, and any other offers she got that were worse than her current best, she says, "Go away; don't come back." The rejected men go back again, and they again propose to their next choices, and this process continues until eventually, every woman has an offer, and when every woman has an offer, every woman is tentatively holding on to a different guy, and at that point, the algorithm stops. At that point, every woman is tentatively paired with a man, and the matchmaker says, "Now the pairing is permanent." This is how you as the matchmaker are going to make the assignments.

Why would this algorithm result in a stable pairing? This is the beautiful part—pure discrete logic. I claim that this process is guaranteed to produce a stable pairing. Proof: Suppose that there was a man i—not me, I, but the variable i—and a woman j, such that i prefers j. I claim [that] j has no interest in i. Why is that? Suppose i preferred j to the mate that he's been assigned; then according to this algorithm, that must have meant that i must have proposed to j earlier, and j must have rejected him. She must have rejected him for somebody, and whoever she wound up [with] at the end had to be at least as good as that, because the women could only trade up along the process. Therefore, even though i is interested in j, j is not interested in i, and therefore, no affairs are going to take place.

By the way, you might ask: Is the stable assignment unique? Is there only one way to pair them up in a stable way? Sometimes it is, such as when man 1 and woman 1 are each other's first choice, and man 2 and woman 2 are each other's first choice, and so on. But often, there are several different ways to create a stable assignment. In fact, it's still an open question in discrete mathematics to define the maximum number of stable pairings that are possible as a function of n. As a matter of fact, I even have a paper on that subject; it's called "How Do I Marry Thee? Let Me Count the Ways."

Who gets the better deal in this algorithm, the men or the women? Thinking about the process, who seems to be in control here, the men or the women? It may seem like since the women get to do all the accepting and rejecting, they get the better deal, but it turns out [that] this algorithm actually favors the men. As it turns out, for each man, among all the women that he could have received in a stable pairing—that might not include his first choice—but among all the women that he could have received in a stable pairing, he gets the woman that he most desires in that set.

This algorithm is called "male optimal," and unfortunately, the algorithm is also "female pessimal," in that each woman receives her least favored mate among all the men she could have been given in a stable pairing. Incidentally, a version of this algorithm is actually used in the medical community to assign medical residents to hospitals. The difference here is that each hospital takes several residents—it's not monogamy here—and takes other factors into consideration, like when married couples are applying together and have to be assigned to the same hospital. A few years ago, they changed the algorithm, so that instead of the algorithm being hospital optimal, it was resident optimal.

The stable marriage problem can be represented with a complete bipartite graph, $K_{N,N}$. Let me define that here. That consists of N vertices representing the men, N vertices representing the women, and we have an edge that connects every man with every woman, but we don't have any edges between men and men [and] we don't have any edges between women and women. For example, here's the graph $K_{3,3}$—3 vertices on the left, 3 vertices on the right, and all of our edges go left to right or right to left; none of them go up and down. After being given everyone's preference list, your job, as matchmaker, is to find a perfect matching in $K_{N,N}$ that is stable. What do I mean by a perfect matching? All it means is: It's a selection of N edges so that every vertex is included on exactly one edge. For instance, here's a perfect matching in $K_{3,3}$. I don't know if it's stable or not, but it's one way of assigning the men to the women: 1 goes to 4, 2 goes to 6, 3 goes to 5. You may ask: How many perfect matchings does $K_{N,N}$ have? They don't have to be stable; just how many perfect matchings will $K_{N,N}$ have? We know this from our basics of combinatorics; there are $N!$ perfect matchings. Since vertex 1 has N choices of an edge, then vertex 2 has $N - 1$ choices of an edge—you can't go to wherever vertex 1 was matched up with—vertex 3 has $N - 2$ choices of an edge, and so on. Therefore, there are $N!$ perfect matches.

Next question: How many perfect matchings does this graph have? Perhaps this represents students sitting at two rows of desks, and everybody has to trade homework papers with someone sitting next to them. This is called the 2-by-4 grid graph. It's got 8 vertices. The 2-by-4 grid graph has five perfect matchings, as shown here. You may ask: How many perfect matchings does the 2-by-N grid graph have? Let's look at them. When $N = 1$, there's just one way. When $N = 2$, we see there are two ways. They can go like this, or they can go like that. When $N = 3$, we see there are three ways. When $N = 4$, we just saw there are five ways; there are five perfect matchings in the 2-by-4 grid graph. When $N = 5$, I'll tell you, there are eight ways. Now look at those numbers: 2, 3, 5, 8—who can't we eliminate? Fibonacci, of course! The number of perfect matchings in the 2-by-N grid graph is f_N, the Nth Fibonacci number. Why is that? If you take a perfect matching in this 2-by-N grid graph, if you chop that matching in half horizontally, look at what you have. You have a 1-by-N board with squares and dominoes. Since we know that the number of 1-by-N boards, the number of 1-by-N strips with squares and dominoes, is the Nth Fibonacci number, there we have it, our N^{th} Fibonacci number.

Suppose you wanted to know how many perfect matchings does the M-by-N grid graph have? When M and N are both odd, the answer is easy: 0. You see why? Here's a graph with 15 points in it; you can't pair them up with 7 ½ edges. You have to have an integer number of edges. The 3-by-5 grid has no perfect matching. The M-by-N grid has no perfect matching if M and N are both odd. On the other hand, when M and N are both even, the answer is very hard. I'll just show it to you here; it is a messy expression. You may ask: How many matchings does the M-by-N grid graph have? They don't have to be perfect matchings; we don't insist that every point be part of a match. How many ways can you do that? This is an unsolved problem. Here is an example of a non-perfect matching in a 4-by-6 grid graph, but I don't even know if anybody knows how many non-perfect matchings are even in a graph of that size because there are a huge number of them.

Here's another nice application of graph theory in social problems. It's called the structural balance problem. What I want you to do this time is finish the following sentences: The friend of my friend is my … friend. The friend of my enemy is my … ; the most likely answer is enemy. The enemy of my friend is my … enemy, but the enemy of my enemy is my … friend. Maybe you've heard all of those expressions before. My question to you is: What if everyone lived their life by these rules, those four rules for living? This problem has actually been addressed by sociologists to explain polarizing behavior. It can be shown, using graph theory, that if everyone lived by those four rules, then only two stable societies could emerge. Either one where everybody was friends with everybody else, so there weren't any enemies to deal with, or the situation where there are two groups of people, say, red folks and blue folks, so that all the red folks are friends with each other, and all the blue folks are friends with each other, but all the red folks are enemies with all the blue folks, and vice versa. You can actually prove that theorem using graph theory, though we won't do that here.

Paul Erdös, whom we met earlier, was the most prolific mathematician in history. In his lifetime, he wrote more than 1400 mathematical papers, more than any other mathematician, and second only to Euler in the number of published pages of mathematical research. Erdös obviously saw mathematics as a social activity and had more than 500 collaborators. In fact, mathematicians have playfully created a graph in his honor. It's called the "collaboration graph," where the vertices represent mathematicians, and two vertices are adjacent if the mathematicians have written a paper together. A person's "Erdös number" is the number of steps that it takes to get to the vertex represented by Erdös. Thus, Erdös has an Erdös number of 0; he's the only one with an Erdös number of 0. Anyone who has written a paper with Erdös has an Erdös number of 1. Anyone else who has written a paper with someone who has written a paper with Erdös has an Erdös number of 2, and so on. My own Erdös number is 3, and it can never be 1, since Erdös died in 1996, but if anyone out there has an Erdös number of 1 and is watching this course, let's talk.

Lecture Nineteen
Tournaments and King Chickens

Scope:

In a tournament with n people, everyone plays everyone else in a game where no ties are possible, and the winner of the match is indicated on a graph. We create a tournament graph where each player is represented by a vertex, and if player x beats player y in the tournament, then an edge is drawn as an arrow pointing from x to y. Using tournament graphs, we prove that no matter who beats whom in the tournament, we will be able to list all the players in some order $v_1, v_2, \ldots, v_n$ so that v_1 beat v_2, v_2 beat v_3, $\ldots$, and v_{n-1} beat v_n. We also prove that the tournament will always contain a "king chicken": player x with the property that for any opponent y, either x beat y or there is some player z for which x beat z and z beat y.

Outline

I. We can use directed graphs to understand tournaments and the Hamiltonian path theorem.

  A. A tournament is a complete graph where every edge has an orientation. An edge that points from i to j can be thought of as player i defeating player j in a tournament where everyone plays everyone else in 1 game.

  B. For example, here is a tournament with 4 players.

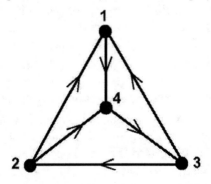

  C. Notice that in this tournament, we have $1 \rightarrow 4 \rightarrow 3 \rightarrow 2$. This is called a (directed) Hamiltonian path because it is a path that goes through every vertex of the tournament.

D. Hamiltonian path theorem: Every tournament has a Hamiltonian path. That is, for $n \geq 1$, for any tournament on n vertices, there is always a sequence of vertices $v_1, v_2, \ldots , v_n$ such that $v_1 \to v_2 \to v_3 \to \ldots \to v_n$.

II. Professor Steve Maurer of Swarthmore College developed the king chicken theorem to explain the pecking orders of chickens.

  A. Definition: In a tournament, x is a king chicken (or king) if for every opponent y, either $x \to y$ or there exists a player z such that $x \to z \to y$. In other words, a king is a player that can walk to any vertex in at most 2 steps.

  B. The king chicken theorem: Every tournament has at least 1 king chicken.

  C. Proof: Let v be a vertex with the maximum outdegree (most victories). Suppose v has k victories and v beat $v_1, v_2, \ldots , v_k$. We claim that v must be a king, since otherwise there would exist another vertex u such that $u \to v$ and $u \to v_1, \ldots , v_k$. But then u beat at least $k + 1$ opponents, contradicting the assumption that v had the most victories.

  D. Theorem: If a player loses, then it must lose to a king.

    1. Proof: Let v be any vertex that has at least 1 loss. Let W be the set of vertices that beat v, and let L be the set of vertices that lost to v. If we just focus on the tournament consisting of the players in W, then by the king chicken theorem, it contains a king (of the set W). Call that king k.

    2. We claim that k is a king of the entire tournament, since k can reach v in 1 step and can reach any vertex in L in at most 2 steps by way of v. Hence v loses to k, a king.

  E. A vertex v is an emperor if $v \to w$ for all w. Clearly, if v is an emperor, then it is also a king. Conversely, if a tournament has exactly 1 king, then that king must also be an emperor.

  F. Corollary: No tournament has exactly 2 kings. Proof: Suppose the tournament has 2 kings, a and b, and say that $a \to b$. Now a had to lose to someone (else he could not be a king). But then a had to lose to a king, and therefore the tournament has at least 1 more king.

III. The preceding theorems suggest many natural questions and extensions.

    A. For example, in a tournament with n players, is it possible for every player to be a king? We have seen that the answer is no when $n = 2$. It is also impossible when $n = 4$. But surprisingly, it is possible for all other values of n.

    B. Moreover, we can build on these results to prove that for $1 \leq k \leq n$, unless $k = 2$ or $n = k = 4$, it is possible to create a tournament with n players that has exactly k kings.

Suggested Reading:

Chartrand, *Introductory Graph Theory*, sec. 7.

Maurer, "The King Chicken Theorems."

West, *Introduction to Graph Theory*, chap. 1.

Questions to Consider:

1. Consider the tournament represented by the oriented graph below.

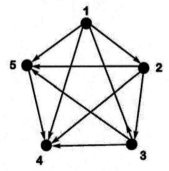

    a. Does the tournament have an emperor?

    b. Find a directed Hamiltonian path.

    c. Which players are king chickens?

2. How many possible tournaments on n vertices exist?

3. For an oriented graph, let $d(x, y)$ be the shortest number of steps to go from x to y, where every step is along an edge in the oriented direction.

    a. In the oriented graph shown in question 1 above, compute $d(3, 2)$.

    b. Prove that in any tournament, for any vertices x and y, $d(x, y) \neq d(y, x)$.

4. In our lecture, we saw that in a tournament, it was possible with 5 players for each player to be tied for first place (i.e., having the most victories). Prove that this is impossible to do with 6 players. Is it ever possible with an even number of players?

Lecture Nineteen—Transcript
Tournaments and King Chickens

We ended our last lecture by talking about the collaboration graph, modeling how mathematicians collaborate to produce new mathematics. In this lecture, we consider the opposite situation, where people are competing against each other. Specifically, we shall apply directed graphs to understand tournaments that arise in sports and other competitions.

There are three common tournament formats: elimination tournaments, as is done in college basketball tournaments; there is the Swiss format, where winners continue to play winners and losers continue to play losers, as is done in many chess tournaments; and in duplicate bridge, sometimes they use round-robin tournaments, where everyone plays everyone else in their division. We're going to focus, in this lecture, on the round-robin situation, where everybody plays everybody else once. Recall from our last lecture, K_m is the complete graph on n vertices where every pair of vertices is adjacent. For example, here is our graph K_4. A tournament is a complete graph where every edge has an orientation; either i points to j or j points to i.

For example, here is a tournament with four players. How do we interpret the tournament? Our interpretation is i points to j, meaning that player i beat player j in a round-robin tournament. You can think of it as i pointing to j, saying, "Ha-ha, I beat you." Or you might look at the i pointing to j kind of looking like a greater-than sign. Here we see that player 1 beat player 4, but player 1 lost to players 2 and 3. The score, or sometimes referred to as the outdegree of a vertex v, is the number of edges leaving v, so the scores for 1, 2, 3, and 4 are, respectively, 1, 2, 2, and 1.

Notice that in this tournament, we have the interesting situation that 1 beat 4, and 4 beat 3, and 3 beat 2. We have a chain that goes all the way through this tournament—1 beat 4, 4 beat 3, 3 beat 2. This is called a directed Hamiltonian path because it's a path that goes through every vertex of the tournament. Does every tournament have a Hamiltonian path? You may remember that when talking about graphs in general, it's a pretty hard question to determine if a graph has a Hamiltonian path or if a graph has a Hamiltonian cycle. Yet you may be surprised to learn, every tournament does have a directed Hamiltonian path. Specifically, we have the Hamiltonian path theorem that says: For any number of players n greater than or equal to 1, every tournament with n vertices, there is always a sequence of vertices, v_1, v_2, through v_n, such that v_1 points to v_2, v_2 points to v_3, and so on down the line points to v_n. In other words, we can list our players in some order, so that player v_1 beat v_2, v_2 beat v_3, and so on all the way down to v_n. For example, in this tournament graph, there are lots of Hamiltonian paths. We see that we can go from 1 to 4 to 3 to 2, but there's also 2 to 1 to 4 to 3; or 2, 4, 3, 1; or 3, 2, 1, 4; or even 4, 3, 2, 1. Those are all directed Hamiltonian paths.

You'd expect that to become much harder and harder as the tournament gets larger and larger, and yet we can prove that there will always be at least one Hamiltonian path in your tournament. We'll prove that by induction on n, the number of players, or the number of vertices. Base case: When $n = 1$, we have a 1-player tournament; there's just 1; that works. It's not very interesting. Let's look at $n = 2$. Then we have 2 players. They play one game; either 1 beat 2 or 2 beat 1. Either way, we have a Hamiltonian path, so our base case is clearly true when $n = 1$ or 2. Next, we state our induction hypothesis. Assume the theorem is true for tournaments with k vertices. Our goal is to prove that it continues to be true for tournaments with $k + 1$ vertices. How do we start the proof? Consider a tournament with $k + 1$ vertices. What do we do now? The goal of induction, if we want to use that induction hypothesis, is we want to reduce that problem from a $k + 1$–sized problem to a problem of size k. How do we reduce it to a problem of size k? Why don't we kick out player $k + 1$? Let everybody play their games, including player $k + 1$, but let's now ignore $k + 1$ and his results. We're removing $k + 1$ from the tournament; this produces a tournament with k vertices. By the induction hypothesis, I know that there's a Hamiltonian path among these k vertices. That's what induction does for us. Hence, there is some arrangement of the vertices so that v_1 beat v_2, v_2 beat v_3, and so on down through v_k. To make my notation easier, let's just assume it happened in numerical order—so 1 beat 2, 2 beat 3, 3 beat 4, and so on down to k.

Now we have to bring $k + 1$ back into the picture, and we want to create a Hamiltonian path that uses all $k + 1$ players. We have three situations to consider. Case 1: If $k + 1$ beat player 1, then we're happy; we have a Hamiltonian path. Do you see it? $k + 1$ beat 1, and 1 beat 2, and 2 beat 3, and so on down the line; that is a Hamiltonian path. If $k + 1$ beats player 1, then we're happy. What's the other obvious situation? If player k beat player $k + 1$ because then 1 beat 2, and 2 beat 3, and 3 beat 4, all the way down to k, and then k beat $k + 1$, and so that would be a Hamiltonian path. Otherwise, if k didn't beat $k + 1$, $k + 1$ must have beat player k. Let's let i be the first player that $k + 1$ beat. We know he at least beat player k; maybe he beat somebody earlier. We know he didn't beat player 1 because we already considered that case, so there has to be some number i between 1 and k so that player $k + 1$ beat player i. We're going to find that first one. In that situation, what do we have? That must have been the case—that player $k + 1$ lost to players 1, 2, 3, up through $i - 1$—but $k + 1$ beat player i; therefore, we can insert it into our Hamiltonian path. All we really needed was that $k + 1$ lost to player $i - 1$ and beat player i. Now, we have a Hamiltonian path using all $k + 1$ players, and that completes our proof by induction.

Our next theorem was used by Professor Steve Maurer of Swarthmore College to explain the pecking orders of chickens. It turns out that for any two chickens, one is always dominant over the other. The dominant one will peck the other one on the head and neck—that's actually where the term "pecking order" comes from. However, it's rarely the case—so I hear—that one chicken dominates all the others. Everyone pecks people and everyone gets pecked by others, so the question is: Is there some way that we might be able to determine which chicken or chickens are the most dominant?

This is actually one of my favorite theorems in graph theory, and it's called—I kid you not—the king chicken theorem. Let me give you a definition: [In] any tournament, we say that x is a king chicken, or simply a king, if x has the following peculiar bragging rights: x can say to any opponent y either x beat y or there is a player z out there such that x beat z and z beat y. If I'm a king and I see any other person out there, I know that I either beat that person or I beat somebody who beat that person. In other words, in a tournament, the king chicken theorem says: There's always a vertex—vertex x, say—from which we can walk to any other point in at most two steps. Starting from a king vertex, you can walk to anywhere in at most two steps. The king chicken theorem says that such a point must always exist.

Here's an example: In the tournament that we've been looking at, player 2 is a king. Why? Because 2 beat 1, 2 beat 4, and though 2 did not beat 3, 2 beat 4 and 4 beat 3, so 2 can get to 3 in two steps. To make life interesting, player 3 is also a king, because 3 beat 1, 3 beat

2, and 3 beat 2 (who beat 4). And even player 4 is a king, because 4 beat 3 (who beat 1), and 4 beat 3 (who beat 2). Now, is everyone a king? No. In this situation, player 1 is not a king. You see that player 1 is not a king because 1 cannot reach player 2 in two steps. He can get to 2 in three steps—he can go 1 to 4 to 3 to 2—but he can't get there in two steps because he lost to 2 and the only player he beat was 4, but 4 did not beat 2. As it turns out, we'll see later, with four players, it's actually impossible for everyone to be a king. But I'm going to prove for you now the king chicken theorem, that every tournament has at least one king.

Unlike the last theorem, the Hamiltonian path theorem that used induction, this one's actually a little hard to prove by induction. The proof, however, is even simpler and very satisfying. Here's how it goes: You have a tournament, and everybody's played their matches, and I claim there has to be at least one king. If you were to just quickly look at the tournament, who would you most likely pick to be king? What would you look at? You would probably choose a vertex that had the most victories, right? If there was a tie? If there were several of them, just pick any one. Let v be any vertex with maximum outdegree. Let's suppose v has k victories, and let's say v beat players v_1, v_2, through v_k. Now does player v have to be a king? You might be surprised to learn the answer is yes. With having the most victories, I'll prove to you that v must be a king. Why? Suppose not: What would it mean for v to not be a king? Then, there would have to exist some vertex u that v couldn't reach in two steps or less, right? There has to be a vertex u such that u beat v and u beat everybody that v beat; u beat v_1, v_2, through v_k. What's wrong with that? Then player u must have beaten at least $k + 1$ opponents, namely, v and all of the people that v beat. But that contradicts the assumption that v had maximum outdegree because u had to do better. Isn't that a gorgeous proof?

The king chicken theorem is a surprising result, with a very elegant proof—at least in my opinion—so what does a mathematician do with it? I want to take time in this lecture to show you. Some mathematicians might go out and try to find situations where it can be applied, but many would look at this theorem, this gorgeous proof, and wonder if it could be pushed further. Are there related theorems that could be proved? In the remainder of this lecture, I want to give you a taste of the sorts of problems that a typical discrete mathematician would naturally consider.

[Let's start] with this theorem, which is in itself a surprising theorem: If a player loses, then that player must lose to a king. Any player that loses has to lose to one of the kings—remember, we might have several kings out there, but if a player loses, they must lose to one of the kings. Here's the proof: Let v be any vertex. Looking at v, we can classify all the points in our graph as being in one of three situations: either it's v, or somebody that beat v, or somebody that lost to v. I'm going to let W be the set of winners—the set of vertices that beat v—and I'm going to let L be the set of losers, the set of points that lost to player v. We could illustrate that as in this diagram. There's v, there's everyone above it—we know that v lost to at least one player, remember—and everyone below it.

Let's first just focus on the set W, just looking at the set of players that beat v—that doesn't include the vertex v. We know that since they formed their own smaller tournament, that tournament has to have a king; at least there has to be a king of W. Let's call that king k. But I claim that k actually has to be a king of the entire tournament, not just the set W. Why? We know that k beat v, and for any vertex in the loser's bracket, anyone that v beat, k can get to them in two steps. Therefore, every point in the tournament can be reached by k in at most two steps. Isn't that neat?

Another definition of strength is a vertex v is called an emperor if v beats W for all W. The emperor defeats all opponents. This is beyond being a king. The emperor can get to everybody in one step. A king can get to everyone in at most two steps. Clearly, if v is an emperor, then it is also a king. In fact, it's got to be the only king, because nobody beat v—there's nobody who could get to v in two steps—so if v is an emperor, it's the only king. Surprisingly, I claim that if a tournament has exactly one king—let's call that king k—then the king must also be an emperor. We can prove that; let's do it. Suppose k is the only king, could k have lost to anyone? I claim k has to be an emperor, but could it have lost to anyone? No, because by our last theorem, if k lost to anyone, it would have had to have lost to another king. But k was the only king; therefore, it couldn't have lost to anyone; therefore, k is an emperor.

Here's another corollary of that theorem. I claim that no tournament can have exactly two kings. No tournament can have exactly two kings. Here's the proof: Suppose the tournament has two kings, a and b. Now a and b had to play each other, so without loss of generality, let's say that player *a* beat player *b*. Now *a* had to lose to somebody, right? Why did *a* have to lose to somebody? If *a* didn't lose to anybody, *b* would not have been a king. But then, that means, by our earlier theorem, since *a* lost to somebody, *a* had to lose to a king, and *a* didn't lose to *b*; consequently, there must be at least one more king in the tournament. Just having two kings, *a* and *b*, ensures the existence of a third king.

Here's another question: In a tournament with *n* players, can every player be a king? Can we have Lake Woebegone, where not only is everyone above average, but everyone's a king? We know that's impossible when you only have 2 players; you can't have both of them being kings. I also claim that that can't happen when you have exactly 4 players. I said that earlier—with 4 players, not everyone can be a king. Let's see why.

When *n* is 4, that means we have 4 players [and] everyone has 3 opponents. I want to prove that not everybody can be a king. Nobody has 3 victories, because if somebody had 3 victories, you'd only have one king, and therefore, not everyone could be king. Nobody has 0 victories, because if someone had 0 victories they can't be king, and therefore, everyone couldn't be a king. Thus, I'll assume that everyone has 1 or 2 victories. Since I have a total of 6 edges in my graph K_4—in my tournament K_4—and everyone has 1 or 2 victories, the only way that could happen is if 2 players have exactly 2 victories and 2 players have exactly 1 victory. That's the only way I can get two 2s and two 1s to add up to 6—the number of edges in the tournament.

Let's say the players who had 2 victories, let's call them *a* and *b*, and let's let the other 2 that had 1 victory, let's call them *c* and *d*. Since *a* and *b* had to play each other, without loss of generality, let's say that *a* beat *b*; now that forces *b*—since it had 2 victories—to beat *c* and *d*. [Player] *a* has 1 other victory, and without loss of generality, let's say that *a* beat player *c*. But then, I claim that *c* can't be a king because *c* would not be able to reach *b* in two steps. Why? We know that *c* lost to *b*. We see that *c* lost to *a*, and in fact, *c* had to beat *d*— that's fine—but *d* did not beat *b*; *b* beats *d*. So we see in this tournament that *c* could not be king. No matter what situation you have here, with 4 players, it's impossible for everyone to be a king. By the way, analogous to the king chicken definition, we could also define an analysis concept for some big loser, called maybe the king turkey—that's my term—that everyone can reach in at most two steps. Naturally, every result that we've obtained for king chickens would apply to king turkeys, too.

Let's go back to our earlier question. In a tournament with n players, is it possible for every player to be a king? We know that you can't have everyone a king when n is 2, and you can't have everyone be a king when n is 4—when you have 4 players—but surprisingly, the answer is yes, for any other number besides 2 or 4, it's possible for everyone to be a king. Let's see how to prove that. Let's look at some small examples first. When $n = 1$, the player is just king of his castle. There's no one to play, so he's a king. When $n = 3$, we have this triangle where a beat b, b beat c, and c beat a, so everybody can reach everybody in two steps, so everyone's a king there.

I've drawn a graph here of K_5, a tournament with 5 players; how do I know that everyone's a king? If you look at how the edges are oriented, you'll notice that every player has exactly 2 victories. We know by the proof of the king chicken theorem that anyone who has the maximum number of victories is guaranteed to be a king, and since all 5 players have 2 victories, we know that everyone could be a king. You'd think we could do that for other tournaments; in fact, when n is odd—when we have 7 players, or 9 players, etc.—then I claim that every vertex—we know that when n is odd, every vertex has degree $n - 1$; everybody plays $n - 1$ people, and $n - 1$ is even. Therefore, the graph K_n, since every vertex has even degree, we know from our very first lecture on graph theory that that tournament would have to have an Eulerian tour.

Let's create an Eulerian tour. Let's go through the graph in a nice Eulerian way, covering every edge and ending where we started. Draw your arrows as you take the tour, and the graph is going to have, at every vertex, $n - 1/2$ edges leaving it and $n - 1/2$ edges entering it. So every vertex has the same score. Every vertex has the same outdegree, and since everyone has the same outdegree, everyone's a king. Now, in fact, everyone not only is a king chicken, [but] everyone is also a king turkey in that situation. I've only shown it to you for the case where you have an odd number of players. Here's the situation when you have an even number of players. Here we have 6 players, and if you look at this tournament, I'll leave it for yourself to verify that every player here is a king. From every vertex, we can reach every other vertex in at most two steps.

In fact, to get all the other even tournaments, starting at 6 as our base case, here's what we're going to do: Suppose I have a tournament T with n players where everyone's a king. Let's say n is an even number and everyone's a king, and now I'm going to prove that I can do it for the next even number. I'm going to do that by adding two new players to join the tournament, x and y. What can we do? How should x and y win or lose their matches to create a situation where everyone's a king in this bigger tournament? Here's what we do: We'll let everyone in T beat x, and we'll let x beat y and nobody else. Player y is going to beat everyone in T, but y loses to x. Then I claim, in this bigger tournament, with $n + 2$ players, everyone is still a king because everyone in T is a king within T, and everyone in T can get to x in one step or y in two steps. Everyone in T is still a king of the bigger tournament. Furthermore, x is a king in this new tournament because x beat y, and y beat everyone in T. Player x can get to anywhere in at most two steps. Player y can get to anywhere in at most two steps also because y beat everyone in T and everyone in T beat x, so y can get to x and everyone else in at most two steps.

Another question we might ask is: For numbers k and n, where k is between 1 and n, does there exist a tournament with n players that has exactly k kings? We're really extending that question. We know the answer is no when k is 2 because no tournament, no matter how many players you have, has exactly 2 kings. We know the answer is no when n is 4 and k is 4 because we proved that with 4 players, you can't have 4 kings. But what's really surprising and cool is the answer is yes for all other values of k and n, you can have a tournament with n players and exactly k kings.

Here's the basic idea behind the proof: Let's look at a specific case; let's prove that there must be a tournament with 8 players that has exactly 5 kings. Now we know there exist tournaments with 5 players where all 5 players are kings. We saw that and proved that earlier. If I want to create a tournament with 8 players and 5 kings, then what do we do? We simply add 3 more players to the mix who all lose to these 5 kings. I don't care what they do among each other, but everyone of the new group loses to these 5 kings. Therefore, none of the 3 new players can be a king, because they'd never be able to get up to beat anybody in that king set. This new tournament will have 8 players and 5 kings—the people that were kings of the first 5 group are still kings when considered among the 8. Where do we go from here? You might try to see what results you can find for directed graphs that are not tournaments, such as when some players don't play each other or when some teams play each other more than once.

We've seen in this lecture that in any tournament, no matter how random the outcomes, your tournament must contain some interesting structures, like a Hamiltonian path or at least one king chicken. In our next lecture, we'll return to the land of undirected graphs, but we'll allow ourselves to put weights on the edges. Our focus will be on a class of graphs that are simple, powerful, efficient and form the backbone of many graphs, as we take on the subject of trees and their applications.

Lecture Twenty
Weighted Graphs and Minimum Spanning Trees

Scope:

Next we "branch off" to describe a special kind of graph that arises in many applications of graph theory. A tree is a connected graph with no cycles. (An unconnected graph with no cycles is called a forest.) Trees have a very simple structure that makes them useful for data storage and communication. For example, one can prove that every tree with n vertices always has exactly $n - 1$ edges. Likewise, every tree must contain at least 1 leaf, a vertex with just 1 neighbor. Finally, it can be shown that in a tree, every pair of vertices is connected by a unique path. We apply these theorems to solve the minimum spanning tree problem, showing how the cheapest connected substructure of a weighted graph can be determined by a greedy algorithm.

Outline

I. A tree is a connected graph with no cycles.

    A. A disconnected graph without cycles is called a forest, and its connected components are trees.

    B. How many trees are there with vertices labeled 1 through n?

        1. Clarification: 2 trees are equal if they have the same set of edges. Thus a tree like 1-2-3 is the same as the tree 3-2-1.

        2. Cayley's formula says that for $n \geq 1$, the number of trees with n vertices is n^{n-2}.

    C. In a tree, a vertex of degree 1 is called a leaf.

    D. Theorem: Every tree T with at least 2 vertices has at least 1 leaf.

    E. Note that when a leaf (and its 1 edge) are removed from a tree, the resulting graph is still a tree. This is useful for many induction proofs about trees.

    F. Theorem: Every tree with n vertices has exactly $n - 1$ edges.

II. Trees are often used as efficient data structures where information is stored at the vertices.

A. For example, when you call someone on your cell phone, your number is picked up by a tower that communicates your number to another tower, and another, until it reaches the top of a tree (called the root) and then finds the person you are trying to reach, who is another leaf of the tree.

B. Trees make excellent data structures for storing words in a dictionary. With about 2^n data points, a search of a binary tree takes only about n steps, compared to about 2^{n-1} steps to search a simple list!

C. The following theorem is useful for communicating between vertices. Theorem: If T is a tree, then any 2 vertices are connected by a unique path.

III. A minimum spanning tree is a tree that connects all the vertices while minimizing the sum of the weights of the edges.

A. Consider a weighted graph like G, the one shown here.

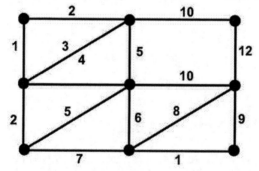

B. This could be a network of roads or computers, and the weight of an edge could represent the cost of traveling from 1 city to another, paving a road between houses, or getting 2 computers to communicate. The problem is to find a spanning tree (a tree that connects all the vertices of G) that minimizes the sum of the weights of the edges.

IV. This problem can be solved using the following greedy algorithm.

A. Choose 8 edges, 1 at a time, from smallest cost to largest cost, where we ignore an edge only if its inclusion would create a cycle.

B. Following this algorithm on the above graph results in the following spanning tree of weight 34.

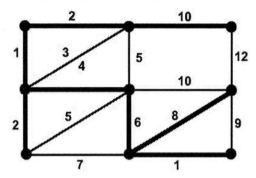

C. Theorem: A tree produced by the greedy algorithm is guaranteed to be a minimum spanning tree.

V. Suppose we wish to know how many spanning trees a graph G has.

A. The answer depends on the adjacency matrix of G and the determinant.

1. The determinant of a 2×2 matrix $\begin{pmatrix} a & b \\ c & d \end{pmatrix}$ is $ad - bc$.

2. The determinant of a 3×3 matrix $\begin{pmatrix} a & b & c \\ d & e & f \\ g & h & i \end{pmatrix}$ is $aei + bfg + cdh - (gec + hfa + idb)$.

3. The formula for the $n \times n$ determinant is the sum of $n!/2$ products minus the sum of $n!/2$ other products—although for $n > 3$, there are quicker ways to compute the determinant without using its formula.

B. The number of spanning trees in a graph is just the determinant of a particular matrix obtained by subtracting the adjacency matrix A from the diagonal matrix D.

1. Let D be the diagonal matrix where the ith number on the diagonal is the degree of vertex i and everything else is 0.

2. Because every row sums to 0, it turns out that the determinant of $D - A$ would always be 0. But if we remove any row and its corresponding column from matrix $D - A$, the determinant of that smaller matrix is equal to the number of spanning trees of G!

VI. The good news about trees is that they are very efficient. The bad news is that they are very vulnerable. If any of your edges breaks, the graph becomes disconnected. Thus, when designing a network, it is generally a good idea to build in some redundancy.

Suggested Reading:

Chartrand, *Introductory Graph Theory*, sec. 4.

Lovász, Pelikán, and Vesztergombi, *Discrete Mathematics*, chaps. 8–9.

Rosen, *Discrete Mathematics and Its Applications*, chap. 9.

West, *Introduction to Graph Theory*, chap. 2.

Questions to Consider:

1. There are essentially 6 different trees with 6 vertices that have fundamentally different pictures. Draw them.

2. Count the ways to label each of the above trees to verify Cayley's formula that there are $6^4 = 1296$ trees with vertex set $\{1, 2, 3, 4, 5, 6\}$.

3. We know that in a tree, there is a unique path connecting any given pair of vertices. Prove the converse theorem: If a graph G has the property that for any pair of vertices x and y, there is a unique path from x to y, then G must be a tree.

4. Find the minimum weight spanning tree for the weighted graph below.

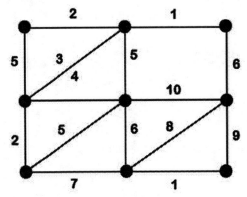

5. Use determinants to compute the number of spanning trees inside the complete (labeled) graph of K_4 below. Why is the answer not a surprise?

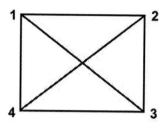

Lecture Twenty—Transcript
Weighted Graphs and Minimum Spanning Trees

In this lecture, we branch off to describe a special kind of graph. These graphs are called trees, and they arise in many real-world problems, from finding the best paths in a network to the efficient storage of data.

Here is the definition of the day: A tree is a connected graph with no cycles. Here is an example of a tree. It's obviously connected; it obviously has no cycles. Here's a non-example. This graph G is not a tree, but it does have connected components—I'm defining that word right here—that are trees. This graph here has 4 connected components. By the way, a graph that has no cycles, whose connected components are trees, we call that, naturally enough, a forest. There are some textbooks out there, by the way, that first define a forest as a graph that doesn't have any cycles, and then they define a tree as a connected forest. I think that's backwards. I think the tree has to come before the forest.

Before we get into theorems about trees, I want to count them; I like combinatorics. How many trees are there that have exactly n vertices? We'll label those vertices 1 through n. Let's call the answer to that combinatorics question T_n. Before we answer that, I have to clarify: What do we mean when we say the two graphs are equal? Officially, two graphs are equal if they have the same vertex and edge set. For example, these first two trees, both labeled 1, 2, 3, and 4, they have the same vertex set. Are they the same tree? They look different; at the bottom, the 3 and 4 go left to right, and on the other one, it goes right to left, but they have the same edge set. Both of those have the edges 1, 2; 2, 3; and 2, 4. Similarly, the third tree on our list also has edges 1, 2; 2, 3; and 2, 4. But the fourth tree on our list is not the same tree because it has an edge like 1, 4, which was not an edge in the earlier trees. Those last two graphs are not equal, but they obviously have the same shape. We use a mathematical term to describe that; they're called "isomorphic." For all intents and purposes they're the same, but they're not formally exactly the same.

Let's answer our question. How many trees have exactly n vertices labeled 1 through n? T_1, the number of trees on one vertex, that's 1. T_2 is also 1; you have an edge that goes from 1 to 2. T_3 is 3 because every tree on 3 vertices looks like a simple path—that's the only way you can draw a tree—but those 3 trees will be different according to what the middle vertex is. Is it 1, or is it 2, or is it 3? There are 3 trees. Another way you can get 3 trees, by the way, is you could say, if order mattered as I went from left to right, how many ways could you label that path? [The answer would be] 3!, right? [There are] 3 choices for the first vertex, 2 for the second, 1 for the last. But every tree is the same as the tree that you get when you flip the tree around. It still has the same set of edges, but whether I look at the tree that goes 1, 2, 3 or the tree that goes 3, 2, 1, those are the same tree. You could quickly say, we have 3!/2—that is, 3 trees on 3 vertices.

How many trees are there on 4 vertices? Let's see, T_4, when we have 4 vertices, we have the path graph, and how many ways can I label a path graph on 4 vertices? [That's] 4!/2, which is 12. What other kind of tree structure can I have with 4 vertices? I can have something that looks kind of like a star, with one point in the middle that's adjacent to the three other points. How many different trees are there? That's all going to depend on what vertex goes in the middle. Either it's vertex 1 that's adjacent to everything else, or 2 that's adjacent to everything else, or 3, or 4, so there are 4 trees like that. Are there any other shapes of trees that we can create? Either it looks like a path, or it looks like a star, and that's it. I don't know of any others, so the total number of labeled trees is 12 + 4, which is 16.

What happens when we have 5 vertices? Then what kinds of shapes can we have? Now there are three different kinds of shapes. It can either be a path graph on 5 vertices, it could be a star with a vertex in the middle, or it could be this kind of T-shaped graph. How many paths are there on 5 vertices? By our earlier logic, 5!/2, which is 60. How many star graphs? There are five choices for what vertex goes in the middle, and then one way to finish everything else off. So there are five star graphs. How many T graphs are there? We've got five choices for that vertex with degree 3, and then it's got three neighbors, one of which has degree 2. There are four choices for what that neighbor's going to be. Then there's another neighbor that's adjacent to that one; there are three choices for what goes there. Then we're essentially done, because it doesn't matter how I label the other two; they're going to be the same tree. There are $5 \times 4 \times 3$, 60 trees on 5 vertices that look like a T; altogether, there are going to be 60 + 5 + 60, 125 different trees on 5 vertices.

Question: How many trees are there with n vertices? Let's look at the pattern. When the number of vertices went from 1 to 5, my answers were 1, 1, 3, 16, and 125. Do those numbers look at all suspicious? When I see 125, I can't help but think 5^3. Then I notice the number behind it is 16, which is 4^2. Behind that is 3^1, 2^0; we even have 1^{-1} power. Putting this altogether, we're inclined to believe Cayley's theorem that says that the number of trees on n vertices is n^{n-2} power. The proof is pretty tricky, so we're not going to do it in this course.

The next definition that I want to give you is: In a tree, a vertex of degree 1—a vertex that's only adjacent to one other part of a tree—is called, naturally enough, what would you guess in a tree? A leaf. A leaf is a vertex of degree 1. Does every tree have a leaf? You bet. In fact, that's what the next theorem says. Any tree with at least 2 vertices has at least 1 leaf.

Here's the proof: Suppose not—the tree is connected, so I can't have any vertices of degree 0, and if it doesn't have any leaves, then it can't have any vertex of degree 1. That would mean that every vertex would have degree at least 2. If every vertex has degree at least 2, as we saw in our proof of the Eulerian graph theorem, there would have to be a cycle in your tree. But trees are not allowed to have cycles. Therefore, there has to be a vertex of degree 1; there must be leaf. That's a theorem so nice I'll prove it twice. Here's another way to prove the theorem, using what we call an "extremal argument." In fact, I'm going to prove something twice as strong, I'm going to prove that every tree has at least 2 leaves. There's another quick proof of that; you could take the one leaf that you found in the last proof, and just keep on walking until you reach a dead end, and that would be the other leaf.

Here's a proof using an extremal argument: Consider in your tree a longest path in T; that is, just find the longest path that you can in the tree. There might be several—there might be a tie for such honors— just pick any path that has the longest length. Let's say it has length k. Let's say it uses vertices v_1, v_2, up to v_k. I claim that vertex v_1— and, by the same reasoning, the vertex v_k—must be leaves of the tree T. Why? We know that v_1 is adjacent to v_2. I claim it can't be adjacent to anything else. For instance, it can't be adjacent to v_3, or v_4, or v_k because then, if it was, we would clearly have a cycle. On the other hand, v_1 can't be adjacent to a vertex that's not on the path because if it was—let's say it was adjacent to some vertex v_0—then v_0, v_1, v_2, up to v_k, that would be a longer path, contradicting the assumption that you started with a longest path. Therefore, v_1 is only adjacent to v_2; therefore, v_1 is a leaf. By the same logic, v_k is a leaf.

Here's a useful observation that we will exploit: Namely, if you have a tree, and you remove any leaf from the tree and the one edge that it has, then the resulting graph is still a tree. Here's a tree, there's a leaf, remove the leaf, and you still have a tree. Next, I claim that every tree with n vertices has exactly $n - 1$ edges. I'm going to prove this by induction on n. You might say I'm using the technique of leaf extraction to prove this. Every tree with n vertices has $n - 1$ edges. Clearly, it's true when n is 1 or 2. We can see that clearly. Next, we state our induction hypothesis: Assume that a tree with k vertices has $k - 1$ edges. Now consider a tree that has $k + 1$ vertices. Remove a leaf v and its one edge. The resulting graph, which I'll call $T - v$, is still a tree, but now it has k vertices. By the induction hypothesis, a tree with k vertices has $k - 1$ edges; therefore, the original tree had to have $k - 1 + 1$ edges, which is k edges, and that concludes our proof.

Trees are often used as efficient data structures where information is stored at the vertices; sometimes raw data is only stored at the leaves. For example, when you call someone on your cell phone, you're actually a leaf on a giant tree. Your number is picked up by a tower that communicates your number to another tower, and another, and another, until it reaches the top of a tree, called the "root," and then it finds the person you are trying to reach, who is another leaf on the tree. Trees make excellent data structures for storing words in a dictionary. Suppose you wanted to create a glossary of key words from this course—the discrete mathematics course—such a list might look like this. Here are several words that I hope you've learned to appreciate in the discrete math course. If you listed them out this way, you'd see there are 15 words on this list, and if you or your computer searched the list to find a given word, it could take anywhere from 1 step to 15 steps, with an average of 8 steps.

On the other hand, it's more efficient to organize your data in the form of a binary tree, like this one. I have the same 15 words organized in this tree, and if you take a look at this tree, you'll notice that, say, at the top of the tree, we have the word "graph," and every word to the left of graph is smaller, comes before it alphabetically. Every word to the right of graph is greater than it alphabetically. That's true of every vertex. When you look to the left, your words come before it in the alphabet; when you go to the right, they come after it in the alphabet.

To find a word, you would start at the top of the tree, and if your word comes before the current word alphabetically, then head down to the left. If it comes after the word, then go down to the right. Once you find your word, then stop. For example, if I'm searching for the word Fibonacci, I compare it with the word graph. Fibonacci comes before graph, so I go to the left. Then, I compare it with discrete. Fibonacci comes after discrete alphabetically, so I move to the right. That puts me at Fermat. Fibonacci comes after Fermat, so I move to the right. Then I find myself at Fibonacci, and I'm happy.

This is, by the way, a lot like the way that you would actually search for a word in a large dictionary. You wouldn't go one page at a time from left to right. Instead, you'd start near the middle, then you'd flip pages back and forth, back and forth, until you found the right page of the dictionary. Notice that it only took 4 steps to find Fibonacci, and that's the worst case. You'll never take more than 4 steps in that tree, as opposed to the list data structure, which took an average of 8 steps. For large amounts of data, the comparison is even better. With about 2^n data points, the binary search takes about n steps, compared to the list, which can take, on average, 2^{n-1} steps.

The following theorem is useful for communicating between vertices: If T is a tree, then I claim that any two vertices on the tree—we know they're connected, not necessarily by a single edge, but by a path; we know there's a way of walking from x to y—I claim there's a unique path that takes us from x to y. Here's the proof: Let x and y be vertices of the tree. Since T is connected, we know that a path P exists from x to y. Here's an abstract sort of path. Can there be another path, let's say, Q, that goes from x to y, like this? No, because if there was, that would create a cycle in T. You could see one giant cycle. In this picture, P and Q have no points in common except for x and y, so the cycle there was easy to see. If they did have points in common, you'd still have a cycle, but it would be a smaller one.

Given a graph G, any tree inside of G that uses all the vertices of G is called a "spanning tree." For example, the graph shown here has several spanning trees, and I've shown them below. Next, we want to consider a very important and practical problem called the minimum spanning tree problem. Consider a weighted graph, like the one we have shown here. This could be a network of roads or computers, and the weight of an edge could represent the cost of traveling from one city to another, or paving a road between houses, or maybe the cost of getting two computers to communicate. We'd like all of our points to be able to communicate with each other, but we want to be as efficient as possible, so we don't need to include every single edge. For maximum efficiency, we wouldn't want to have any cycles, because an edge from a cycle can be removed, and everything would stay connected. The algorithm I'm going to show you to solve this problem was originally developed for telephone networks at Bell Laboratories. It's called the spanning tree problem: Find a spanning tree—a tree that connects all the vertices of G—that minimizes the sum of the weights of the edges. Let's find a spanning tree in the graph; here's a quick one. One way would be to connect all the vertices like this, using this Hamiltonian path; it's kind of S-shaped. That's a tree—it's a spanning tree—and if we add up the weights on all the edges, we get 44.

Can we do better? Here's another spanning tree. It's not a Hamiltonian path. It kind of looks like a W there. We're using all 9 vertices; there should be 8 edges in that spanning tree, and when we sum up the weights on this one, we get a total cost of 43. Can we do better? Let's try and be more systematic. We know that a tree on 9 vertices has to have exactly 8 edges. Our spanning tree's going to have to have 8 edges, so why don't we just choose the 8 cheapest edges—the edges with the smallest weights on them, the smallest costs—and be done with it? Choose the 8 cheapest edges; there we go. Unfortunately, if you do that in this example, you don't get a tree. You see we've got at least one cycle in this graph; I see an isolated vertex over there, so nice try, but no tree.

Here's a better idea; let's proceed by a greedy algorithm. Let's still try to choose the 8 cheapest edges. We're going to go one at a time, from cheapest to most expensive, and we're going to just keep taking, and taking, and taking, except we won't take an edge if it creates a cycle. We're just going to be greedy, except when we create a cycle, in which case, we'll skip over it and we'll try something else.

For example, in this graph, I'll take the cheapest edge. I've got two edges with weight 1; take either one, literally, either 1. You picked 1. Now what's the next cheapest edge? It's the other 1; we'll take that. Then let's see, I'll take one of those 2s; I'll take another one of those

2s. Now let's see; I've got a 3, but can I take the 3? I can't take the 3 because that would create a cycle with that 1 and 2. I'll permanently ignore that one. Next I'll go to the 4. I can take that; that doesn't cause a cycle. How about a 5? If I take that 5 there, that would create a cycle with the 1, 2, 4, so I can't do that one. If I take that 5 there— no, that would create a cycle with the 2 and the 4, so I can't take that one either. Next we go for the 6. I can take that; that doesn't create a cycle. The 7—no, that creates a cycle. How about the 8? The 8 is great. I can take that, no problem. The 9—no, I don't think so; that 9 creates a cycle with the 1 and the 8. I can't choose this 10 because that would create a cycle, but I can take that 10; that won't create a cycle. Whew! I've chosen 8 edges, and let's see how I've done. It's a spanning tree, there are no cycles in this graph, it's connected. The total weight of this one is 34.

Question: Is our spanning tree optimal? The answer is yes. Will this approach always produce a minimum-weight spanning tree? Again, it may surprise you, but the answer is yes. The greedy algorithm that we just went through, also known as Kruskal's algorithm, works every time, and if you don't believe me, here's the proof. In my proof, I'm going to suppose that all the weights of the edges are different. If any of the weights aren't different, we can tweak them by a tiny amount and that won't change the answer. Okay, so here we go. Suppose G has n vertices, then the greedy algorithm will create a tree T with edges e_1, e_2 and so on, where the weight of the first edge will be strictly less than the weight of the second edge it chooses, and so on up to the last edge that it chooses. I claim that the greedy tree has minimum weight.

Proof by contradiction: Suppose, to the contrary, that there is a tree T^* with smaller weight, so the star means, "I'm the best; I'm the cheapest tree around." I'm going to prove that that is impossible. Let e_k be the first edge in T, the greedy tree, that's not in T^*. T^* has edges e_1 up through e_{k-1}, but it does not have e_k. Now, we insert e_k into T^* to create the graph $T^* + e_k$. This graph will have a unique cycle C. There must be an edge e^* on the cycle C that's not e_1, or e_2, or e_{k-1}, or e_k. Why? Because otherwise, that cycle would be in T, and we know that T doesn't have any cycles.

By the greedy algorithm, I claim that the weight of e_k is less than the weight of e^*. Why? Because our greedy algorithm, after it chose e_1 through e_{k-1}, it could have then chosen e^*. It could have; it wouldn't have created a cycle because T^* has e_1 through e_{k-1} and e^*, so it could have chosen e^*, but it didn't. Instead, it chose the edge e_k. Why did it do that? Because it's greedy, it must have been because the weight of e_k was less then the weight of e^*.

If we remove e^*, then the cycle C disappears, and we have a new tree, T^{**}, whose weight is the weight of T^* + the weight of e_k − the weight of e^*. Since the weight of e_k is less than the weight of e^*, then T^{**} has a smaller total weight than T^*, contradicting the assumption that T^*—despite all its bragging—was the minimum spanning tree, and that's the proof. A minimum spanning tree is found every time by the greedy algorithm.

Speaking of spanning trees, here's another combinatorial graph theory problem with a beautiful answer. Suppose we're given a graph G—like the one below—and we wish to know how many spanning trees it has. There's a beautiful answer that depends on the adjacency matrix of G and something called the "determinant." The determinant of a matrix is a number that reveals a lot of information about a matrix—most of which we won't go into here. The determinant of a 2-by-2 matrix—$\begin{bmatrix} a & b \\ c & d \end{bmatrix}$—is very easy to compute.

It has determinant $ad - bc$. The determinant of a 3-by-3 matrix is trickier, but it's still not too bad, and we present the formula here. One way to remember it is if you put two copies of the matrix side by side, then the determinant is the sum of these three products, $aei + bfg + cdh$, − the sum of these three products, gec, hfa, and idb. The formula for the n-by-n determinant is much more complicated. It's the sum of $n!$ over two products − the sum of $n!$ over two other products. Although, when n is bigger than 3, there are quicker ways to compute the determinant without using its formula.

It turns out that the number of spanning trees in a graph is just the determinant of a particular matrix, and I'll tell you how to create that matrix. Suppose that a graph G has adjacency matrix A—we've run into the adjacency matrix before—let D be the diagonal matrix, where the ith number on the diagonal is the degree of vertex i. Everything else in the matrix is 0. For example, the graph we saw earlier that had 8 spanning trees has this diagonal matrix and this adjacency matrix. Here's the cool part: Create the matrix $D - A$—so in this example, here's our D matrix, there's our A matrix, there's the matrix $D - A$. Now, $D - A$, every row is going to sum to 0, like we have here. It turns out because of that, the determinant of $D - A$ will always be 0. But if we remove the last row and the last column of $D - A$, then believe it or not, the determinant of that matrix is always equal to the number of spanning trees of G. Here's our $D - A$ matrix, we get rid of the last row and the last column, that gives us a 3-by-3 matrix, and adding up and subtracting our products—let's see, $2 \times 3 \times 2$ is 12, $+ -1 \times -1 \times 0$ (that's 0), + another 0, $-$ the sum of $0 + 2 + 2$, and that gives us 8, which is the number of spanning trees of G. There's our graph G, there are its 8 spanning trees, and it's counted by that determinant.

The good news about trees is that they're very efficient. The bad news is that they're very vulnerable. If any of your edges break, the graph becomes disconnected. Thus, when designing a network, it's generally a good idea to build in some redundancy so that everything can stay connected while some items are being repaired. For example, we might allow some cycles or allow more than one edge to connect two vertices. But a minimum spanning tree provides an efficient foundation on which to build your network.

I'd like to end this lecture with a poem that I wrote just for this occasion. I call it "Trees":

> I think that I shall never see
> A graph as lovely as a tree,
> Where every leaf stays on the tree,
> Although it's cold out, 1 degree.
> And if two points would like to speak,
> They always can, and it's unique.
> Theorems are proved by fools like me,
> But only graphs can make a tree.

Lecture Twenty-One
Planarity—When Can a Graph Be Untangled?

Scope:

Next we introduce the notion of a planar graph, which is a graph that can be drawn on a sheet of paper in such a way that none of its edges cross, and we prove (another!) theorem due to Euler that says that if a connected planar graph has n vertices, e edges, and f faces, then $n - e + f = 2$. The same formula applies to the vertices, edges, and faces of polyhedra. As a consequence, we show that a planar graph with n vertices has at most $3n - 6$ edges. This leads us to discover 2 graphs that cannot be straightened out, which are an essential part of all nonplanar graphs.

Outline

I. Some graphs are more useful when they can be drawn without crossing edges (e.g., graphs of circuit boards or highway systems).

  A. Definition: A planar graph is a graph that can be drawn in such a way that no edges cross.

   1. For example, all trees are planar graphs.
   2. K_4 is planar since it can be drawn as a triangle with a vertex inside it, with none of the 6 edges crossing.

  B. Every planar graph divides the plane into regions or faces, including the external face. For example, this graph has 6 faces.

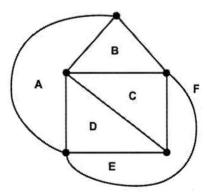

II. Euler's planar graph theorem: If G is a connected plane graph with n vertices, e edges, and f faces, then $n - e + f = 2$. For example, the graph above has $n - e + f = 5 - 9 + 6 = 2$.

   A. Euler's theorem also applies to 3-dimensional objects (called polyhedra) like the cube, which has 8 vertices, 12 edges, and 6 faces. Notice that $n - e + f = 8 - 12 + 6 = 2$.

   B. Euler's theorem can also be used to show that it is impossible to construct Venn diagrams with 4 (or more) circles.

III. Our next theorem proves that planar graphs cannot have too many edges.

   A. Theorem: If G is a planar graph with $n \geq 3$ vertices and e edges, then $e \leq 3n - 6$.

   B. The theorem fails when $n = 1$ or 2 since K_1 and K_2 have $e > 3n - 6$.

   C. For the proof of this theorem, we consider 2 cases: Either G is connected or G is not connected.

   D. Notice that $e = 3n - 6$ is achievable, for example, on the graphs K_3 ($n = 3$, $e = 3$) and K_4 ($n = 4$, $e = 6$).

   E. Corollary: K_5 is nonplanar. The proof is simple. K_5 has $n = 5$ vertices and $e = 10$ edges. Since $e > 3n - 6 = 9$, K_5 cannot be planar.

IV. The converse statement—if $e \leq 3n - 6$, then G is nonplanar—is false.

   A. For example, the complete bipartite graph $K_{3,3}$ (pictured below) has $n = 6$ vertices and $e = 9 < 12 = 3n - 6$ edges. Nevertheless, $K_{3,3}$ is nonplanar.

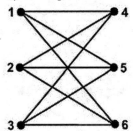

   B. In fact, K_5 and $K_{3,3}$ are the simplest nonplanar graphs in that every nonplanar graph must contain 1 of them.

C. Specifically, Kuratowski's theorem says that every nonplanar graph contains inside it K_5 or $K_{3,3}$ or a subdivision of K_5 or $K_{3,3}$. A subdivision of a graph is the same graph with some new vertices of degree 2 added to some of the edges of G.

Suggested Reading:

Chartrand, *Introductory Graph Theory*, sec. 9.

Lovász, Pelikán, and Vesztergombi, *Discrete Mathematics*, chap. 12.

Rosen, *Discrete Mathematics and Its Applications*, chap. 8.

Scheinerman, *Mathematics: A Discrete Introduction*, sec. 52.

West, *Introduction to Graph Theory*, chap. 6.

Questions to Consider:

1. If G is a planar graph with 9 vertices and 15 edges, how many faces must it have?

2. Show that the graph below is planar.

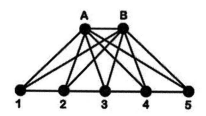

3. In the graph below (sometimes called the Petersen graph), every cycle has length at least 5. Use this fact and Euler's planar graph theorem to prove that it is nonplanar.

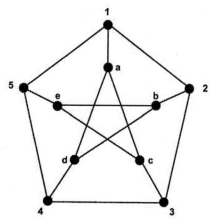

4. Another way to prove that the Petersen graph is nonplanar is to find a subdivision of K_5 (below) or $K_{3,3}$ (shown in section IV of the outline above) inside it. Why could it not have a subdivision of K_5 in it? Find a subdivision of $K_{3,3}$ in it.

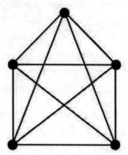

Lecture Twenty-One—Transcript
Planarity—When Can a Graph Be Untangled?

When drawing a typical graph, you're allowed to let edges cross. For example, the graph K_4 can be drawn like this. It has just 4 vertices. Even though the edges cross in the middle, it only has 4 vertices, so don't count the place where they cross in the middle. But some graphs are more useful when they can be drawn without any crossing edges. This is important in computer hardware, where it's expensive to add extra layers to a computer circuit board.

For example, here we have a circuit that traces the one side of this board, and then there's a layer of insulation, and then there are more circuit paths on this side of the circuit board. Or, to give a larger example, the graph of a highway system is much more complicated and expensive if you need overpasses and offramps to keep the roads from crossing. The definition of the lecture is this: A "planar graph" is a graph that can be drawn in such a way that no edges cross. For example, trees are planar graphs—like the one we have here—since they can always be drawn so that none of their edges cross. Although we drew it originally with crossing edges, nevertheless, K_4 is planar because it can be drawn in a way where none of the edges cross. It can be drawn like this or it could be drawn like this—like this little tetrahedron. In fact, a planar graph can always be drawn using only straight lines. That's tricky to prove, but it's true.

For example, this graph here, which looks like K_5 with one missing edge, has a plane graph. That's what we call it when you've drawn it in such a way that none of the edges cross. This is an example of a plane graph, which means that that graph is planar. Or we could straighten out the edges so that it looks like this instead. But as we shall see, the graph K_5, the complete graph on 5 vertices where all the pairs of vertices are connected, is nonplanar—definitely not planar. But first we present Euler's planar graph theorem. This will be our third and final theorem named after Euler. The other two were the Eulerian graph theorem and his generalization of Fermat's theorem.

Here's what Euler's planar graph theorem says: Every plane graph divides the plane into regions, or faces, including the external face. For example, here's a plane graph, none of the edges cross, and this graph has 6 faces, including that external face, f. The external face may seem a little funny, but if you take your graph and you wrap it onto the surface of a sphere, then the external face looks just as normal as all the other faces. Here's what Euler's planar graph theorem says: If G is a connected plane graph, with n vertices, e edges, and f faces, then $n - e + f = 2$. It's a graph theoretic formula to marvel at: $n - e + f = 2$. We'll prove this by induction on e—the number of edges in the graph.

Starting with the base case where e is 0, if I've got a connected graph with no edges, then what does my graph look like? A single point. It has 1 vertex, no edges, and 1 face, so $n = 1$, $e = 0$, $f = 1$, so $n - e + f$ would equal 2. There's the base case. Now we state our induction hypothesis: Assume it's true for any graph where the number of edges is equal to k. Now consider a graph G, a connected plane graph, that has $k + 1$ edges, that is, where $e = k + 1$. I'll break this part of the proof into two cases: the first case, the graph is a tree, and the second case, when the graph is not a tree. The case where it's a tree, I'm not even going to even need induction here. Since G is a tree with n vertices, then we know it has how many edges? [It's] $n - 1$. How many faces does a tree have? It just has 1. Therefore, $n - e + f$ is going to equal $n - (n - 1) + 1$, which equals 2.

Case 2: Suppose G is not a tree—again, G is a connected plane graph, with $k + 1$ edges. In the spirit of induction, what am I going to do? I'm going to find a way to reduce it to the case where it has k edges. My graph has n vertices, $k + 1$ edges, and f faces. I want to show that $n - e + f$ will equal 2 in this case. Since the graph is connected and it's not a tree, then it has to contain a cycle. Let's call that cycle C. Take that cycle C and remove any edge you want from C to obtain a smaller graph, and we'll call that smaller graph G'. G had n vertices, and the number of edges was $k + 1$—$e = k + 1$— and it had f faces. What's G' going to look like? I haven't removed any vertices, so the number of vertices is still n. I removed one edge, so instead of having $k + 1$ edges, I now have k edges.

What happened to the faces? If you think of every edge as separating two faces—at least that's the case when the edge appears on a cycle. It's separating two faces; one face contains water and the other face contains water. You get rid of the dam that's separating them and the water flows together. You now have one fewer face than you had before. Instead of having f faces, you now have $f - 1$ faces. This new graph, G', is a plane graph; it's still connected because I took an edge away from a cycle. You can always remove an edge from a cycle and keep the graph connected. It has now how many edges? [It has] k edges. Since it has k edges, our induction hypothesis applies to it that says n, its number of vertices, $-k$, its number of edges, $+ (f - 1)$, its number of faces, is equal to 2. I could rewrite that statement as $n - (k + 1) + f = 2$. When I go back to my original graph, $k + 1$ was the number of edges, f is the number of faces, n was the number of vertices, so we have $n - e + f = 2$, as desired.

Euler's theorem also applies to three-dimensional objects, too, called polyhedra. Take this cube here. This is a polyhedron, and it has how many vertices? It has 8 vertices, these 4 on the top [and] these 4 on the bottom. It has how many faces? It has 6 faces; it's like a 6-sided die—1, 2, 3, 4, 5, and 6. How many edges does it have? It has 4 edges that run across the top, 4 edges that run across the bottom, and 4 edges that come down, giving me 12 edges altogether $(4 + 4 + 4)$. Now when we calculate $n - e + f$, we get $8 - 12 + 6$, which equals 2.

You can also draw the planar graph of a cube by squashing it onto a flat piece of paper. This cube is pretty solid, so I'm not going to be able to squash it, but you could look at the picture here. The cube is going to go from this to this. What you can't see is the bottom face of the cube; that disappears and becomes the external face of the planar graph. That's why Euler's theorem will apply both to polyhedra and to the planar graphs.

Let's switch topics. We're still talking about planar graphs, but here's a planar graph we've had the pleasure of encountering earlier, in our lecture on the principle of inclusion-exclusion. Here we have a Venn diagram with 3 circles. A Venn diagram separates your total region into 8 different regions, depending on—if I call my circles A, B, and C—are my points in just A, just B, just C, or are they in A and B and not C? Or maybe they're not in any of the 3. How many ways can I decide whether a point is in A or not, B or not, or C or not? [That would be] $2 \times 2 \times 2$—8 ways of doing it. A Venn diagram with 3 circles is going to have 8 regions, just like we have here.

Now, I'm going to draw it in such a way that whenever 2 circles intersect, they intersect at 2 points, and we call both of those points vertices. We're just going to stick a vertex wherever 2 circles intersect. This Venn diagram, you can count, has exactly 6 vertices, it has 12 edges, and it has—as we said earlier—8 faces. When we calculate $n - e + f$, we get $6 - 12 + 8$; we get 2. Hurray for Euler's planar graph theorem; it works here.

Have you ever seen a Venn diagram with 4 circles? You probably haven't because they're actually impossible to draw. Let me prove to you that it's impossible to draw a Venn diagram with exactly 4 circles. First of all, how many faces would it have to have? How many regions would it have to have? Just like with 3 circles, you had to have 8 faces, with 4 circles, you'd have to have 16 faces, 2^4, because a point is either in A or not, B or not, C or not, or D or not. It has to have 16 faces, 1 for every subset of the 4 circles. What else? How many vertices is it going to have? Each pair of circles creates 2 vertices. How many pairs of circles are there? I have 4 circles; how many ways can I choose 2 of them? [That's] $\binom{4}{2}$ ways; $\binom{4}{2}$ is 6, and since every pair of circles creates 2 vertices, that gives me 12 vertices. How many edges do we have? Take a look; how many edges are we going to have to have? Wherever 2 circles intersect, at every vertex, how many edges come out of that vertex? Every vertex has degree 4. How does that tell me the number of edges? By the handshake theorem, the sum of the degrees of the vertices is twice the number of edges. What would that tell us here? We have 12 vertices; each has degree 4. The sum of the degrees of the vertices—that would be 48—that's equal to twice the number of edges. If twice the number of edges is 48, then the number of edges must be 24. We've calculated the number of vertices, edges, and faces. When we calculate $n - e + f$, we have $12 - 24 + 16$, and that gives us 4, which is not equal to 2. That means that a Venn diagram for 4 circles would actually be impossible because if it were possible, $n - e + f$ would have to equal 2. Here, it's equal to 4, so, we can't draw a Venn diagram for 4 circles. A similar argument will show that you can't create one for 5 or more circles either.

Our next theorem proves that planar graphs can't have too many edges. If you just have too many edges, then you inevitably are going to have crossings, and you don't like that. More precisely, if G is a planar graph with at least 3 vertices—if it has n vertices where n is at least 3—and let's say it has e edges, then in order to be planar, we must have $e \leq 3n - 6$. In a planar graph, the number of edges is at most $3 \times$ the number of vertices $- 6$.

First of all, we need the condition that n is at least 3. The theorem is false when $n = 1$ or 2. When $n = 1$, then our graph would look like K_1, a single point, and there's no way e is going to be less than -3—

we can't have a negative number of edges. In the graph K_2 that has 2 vertices and 1 edge, then here, $3n - 6$ would be 0, and the number of edges is 1, and that's bigger than $3n - 6$. The theorem doesn't work when n is less than 3.

Next, I'm going to break this proof down into two cases. Either the graph is connected or the graph is not connected. Let's first consider the case where the graph is connected. Suppose G has n vertices, e edges, and f faces; then by Euler's planar graph theorem, since G is connected, we can say that $n - e + f = 2$. Now, [we] create what I call the "edge-face matrix M" that will contain e rows and f columns—it's going to be an e-by-f matrix—where the (i, j) entry of the matrix is 1 if edge number i borders face number j. Otherwise, we put a 0. We've got a matrix full of 0s and 1s, where the (i, j) entry is 1 if the ith edge boarders the jth face. Take a look at this example. Here's our graph G, and here is its edge-face matrix M. The graph has 7 edges, and it has 3 faces, so it's a 7-by-3 matrix. Let's look at the first edge. That first edge borders face number 2 and the external face, face number 1. It doesn't border face number 3, and that's why that first row of the edge-face matrix would be 1, 1, 0. Or you could take a look at a typical face, like face number 2 has what edges bordering it? It has edges 1, 2, and 3 bordering it, and therefore, if I look down column number 2, I'm going to see that it has 1s in rows 1, 2, and 3, and 0s everywhere else.

What I'm going to do now is I'm going to count the number of 1s in my matrix. I'm going to do this counting in two different ways. I'm going to count the 1s row by row, and I'm going to count the 1s column by column. I'm interested in the total number of 1s in the matrix, and I'm going to call that total x. What can we learn about x as we count the 1s row by row? What can you say? For any edge, how many faces does it border? In our example, it usually borders 2 faces, but it's also possible for an edge to border just 1 face. Look at edge number 7 there; you'll see it's inside of face 3. That's the only face that it borders, so its row looks like 0, 0, 1. In general, for any graph, an edge will either border 2 faces or 1 face. Therefore, if I sum up all the 1s row by row, how many 1s am I going to have? I'll have at most 2 times the number of rows, that is, at most 2 times the number of edges. Therefore, $x \leq 2e$.

On the other hand, if I count my edges column by column, what can we say about any given face? For any given face, how many edges border it? I'm using the fact that n is at least 3 here, so take a look at a typical face, like face number 2; it looks like a triangle. It's going to have at least 3 edges bordering it. Or face number 3, that looks like a square with something inside of it. It's going to have at least 4 edges bordering it. But the smallest possible face that I could have is a triangle, and therefore, every face borders at least 3 edges. Therefore, if I'm counting my 1s column by column, the total number of 1s, x, is going to be at least $3f$ because every face has at least 3 edges on it. Therefore, since $x \leq 2e$, and $x \geq 3f$—x must live between $3f$ and $2e$. That is, $3f \leq x, \leq 2e$.

Now, if I get the x out of there, I just have the inequality $3f \leq 2e$. But let's get rid of f. We know from Euler's equation, $n - e + f = 2$, which means that $f = 2 - n + e$. Replacing f with that tells me that $3(2 - n + e) \leq 2e$, which says that $6 - 3n + 3e \leq 2e$, and subtracting $2e$ from both sides tells us that $e \leq 3n - 6$.

Are we done? Almost, but we only did the case where G is connected. On the other hand, if G is not connected, here we just add the edges to G to create a graph G' that's connected with, let's call it, e' edges. The graph is still planar, just like in the picture here. If the graph isn't connected, add some edges so that it becomes connected, and now we know from case 1, since this is a connected planar graph, that $e' \leq 3n - 6$. Therefore, the number of edges in the original graph, e, was less than e', so that's still less than or equal to $3n - 6$.

You may ask: Can e actually equal $3n - 6$? The answer turns out to be yes, [it] can. For instance, if we're looking at the triangle K_3, that's 3 and that's got 3 edges and 3 vertices, so $e = 3n - 6$ here. In the graph K_4, that has 4 edges and 6 vertices, here we also have $e = 3n - 6$, as well.

The theorem says: If G is planar with n vertices and e edges, then $e \leq 3n - 6$. The contrapositive of this theorem says for any graph with at least 3 vertices, what would the contrapositive say? If the number of edges is bigger than $3n - 6$, then the graph is non-planar. As a corollary, we have that K_5—the complete graph on 5 vertices—is definitely not planar. The proof is simple: K_5 has 5 vertices, and it has 10 edges. Since the number of edges, e, is bigger than $3n - 6$—$3n - 6 = 9$—then K_5 must not be planar.

What about the converse theorem? What is the converse theorem? The converse says: If the number of edges is less than or equal to

$3n - 6$, then G is planar. Is that converse statement true or is it false? It turns out, it's false. In fact, the counterexample I'll give you is one that you might have seen as a kid, [and] you actually saw it in our lectures when we were talking about the stable marriage problem. It's the graph $K_{3,3}$. In the stable marriage discussion, we had 3 men on the left, 3 women on the right, and we drew an edge between every possible man and woman. $K_{3,3}$ is called the "complete bipartite graph," with 3 vertices on the left and 3 on the right. What makes it complete is that every possible edge that can be drawn from left to right is drawn. I remember seeing this graph when I was a kid because they'd give us this little puzzle in this activity book and they'd say, "We've got 3 houses here [and] 3 utility companies there; connect every house with a utility company in such a way that the edges don't cross." I remember working on that problem, and working on that problem, and I just couldn't do it. Finally, I'd look up in the back of the book, and it would say one of two things. It would either say, "There is no answer; sorry, don't you feel foolish?" or they'd give some cheap answer like one of the edges you have to kind of dig below and go underground and go up. So it wasn't being drawn in the plane. You might say I was a "complanar" about that problem.

Here's a graph $K_{3,3}$, and in this graph, we have how many vertices? We have 6 vertices. We have how many edges? [Since] $3 \times 3 = 9$, the number of edges, 9, is less than $3n - 6$, which is 12. Nevertheless, $K_{3,3}$ is nonplanar, and here's the proof: Suppose to the contrary that $K_{3,3}$ is planar. If it was planar, and we could straighten it out into some kind of plane graph, then how many faces would it have? We know the number of vertices, n, is 6, and we know the number of edges is 9—that's given to us—so by Euler's theorem, we know the number of faces could be calculated as $2 - n + e$. That's $2 - 6 + 9$, which is 5. In the plane graph, it would have to have 5 faces.

If I created an edge-face matrix for $K_{3,3}$, it would have 9 rows, 1 for each edge, and 5 columns, one for each face. If I count the number of 1s in the edge-face matrix—call that total number of 1s x—then just like before, counting it row by row, every row has at most two 1s in it, that is, $x \leq 2$ times the number of rows—$2 \times e$—and e here is 9, so that says that $x \leq 18$. On the other hand, for the graph $K_{3,3}$, unlike your typical planar graph, where your smallest face might be a triangle, if you look at $K_{3,3}$, because it's bipartite, it's impossible to have a triangle. If you go from the left to the right and then to the left again, you can't hook up with that original vertex; you have to go to the right again. Every cycle would have to have at least 4 edges. If every face has at least 4 edges, then in that case, $x \geq 4f$, and f is 5, so that would say that $x \geq 20$. Now we have a contradiction, because on the one hand, we saw that x was less than or equal to 18, on the other hand, x would have to be greater than or equal to 20. Therefore, you can't draw an edge-face matrix at all; therefore, your graph is not planar.

We've seen two graphs that are nonplanar, K_5 and $K_{3,3}$. As a matter of fact, K_5 and $K_{3,3}$ are the simplest nonplanar graphs out there in a very real sense, in that every nonplanar graph has to contain one of them. Specifically, this is called Kuratowski's theorem. Every nonplanar graph contains inside it either K_5—living somewhere in your graph—or $K_{3,3}$, or a subdivision of K_5 or $K_{3,3}$. What's a subdivision? Here is a subdivision of K_5; here is a subdivision of $K_{3,3}$. A subdivision of a graph is just taking that graph and putting pimples on it. In other words, I've added a bunch of vertices along some edges, but those vertices that I added only have degree 2. In other words, I can't put a vertex where two lines might cross in the graph. I'm just adding—I'm subdividing one of the edges into smaller and smaller parts. There is a subdivision of K_5, a subdivision of $K_{3,3}$, and every nonplanar graph either contains K_5, or $K_{3,3}$, or one of its subdivisions. We won't prove Kuratowski's theorem, but it's definitely an intriguing result.

Incidentally, in case you were wondering where the "K" came from in the complete graph, like K_5, or the complete bipartite graph, $K_{3,3}$, it's not some kind of German word for "complete," but rather, it's in honor of Kuratowski and the theorem that we just described. Speaking of complete graphs, this completes our lecture on planar graphs. But planar graphs will play a key role in our next lecture on map coloring, leading to one of the most famous problems in graph theory, the 4-color theorem.

Lecture Twenty-Two
Coloring Graphs and Maps

Scope:

One of the most famous problems from graph theory is the 4-color theorem, which says that a map of states can always be colored in such in a way that no adjacent states are assigned the same color and that we need at most 4 colors to achieve this. This problem was unsolved for centuries and has only been proved recently with considerable computer assistance. After showing which graphs can be colored using at most 2 colors, and how any map can be converted to a planar graph, we present the essential theorems of planar graph coloring. Next we provide a brilliant proof of the 5-color theorem, followed by a flawed proof of the 4-color theorem. It took experts 10 years to detect the flaw, then nearly 100 years to finally prove the theorem true.

Outline

I. Planar graphs play an important role in proper colorings of graphs and maps.

   A. Given a graph G, a coloring of G is obtained by assigning a color to every vertex (repetition of colors allowed). It is called a proper coloring if no adjacent vertices have the same color.

   B. We say that a graph is k colorable if it can be properly colored using at most k colors. The smallest number k for which a graph G is k colorable is called the chromatic number of G. For example, the complete graph K_n has chromatic number n, since every vertex must be given a different color.

   C. A closely related idea is proper map coloring, where every state is assigned a color so that no states that share a common border are given the same color. (We assume that states are connected regions and that adjacent states need to have more than a point in common; they must share a common boundary.)

   D. The 4-color theorem says that every map can be properly colored using at most 4 colors. It was one of the most famous unsolved problems in mathematics until a few decades ago, and its final proof was controversial. Its proof took hundreds of pages, so we will not prove it here, but we will prove the 5-color theorem.

E. We can represent any map-coloring problem as a vertex-coloring problem by creating the dual graph of the given map: We insert a vertex at the capital of each state and connect 2 capitals with an edge if they share a common border. A proper coloring of the original map corresponds to a proper coloring of the dual graph, which is always planar.

F. Thus to prove the 5-color theorem for maps, it suffices to prove the 5-color theorem for coloring the vertices of a planar graph.

II. Before we prove the 5-color theorem, we establish the following lemma (or theorem): Every planar graph G must contain a vertex of degree ≤ 5.

III. The 6-color theorem: For any planar graph G, the vertices of G can be properly colored with at most 6 colors.

A. Proof (by induction on n, the number of vertices): Base case. The theorem is clearly true when G has at most 6 vertices.

B. By the induction hypothesis (IHOP): Assume the theorem is true for planar graphs with k vertices. Our goal is to prove it for planar graphs with $k+1$ vertices.

C. Let G be a planar graph with $k+1$ vertices. By our lemma, there is a vertex v with degree at most 5. Temporarily remove v (and its edges) from G to produce graph $G - v$.

D. Since $G - v$ is still planar and has k vertices, then by IHOP, we can properly color $G - v$ with at most 6 colors.

E. Bringing v back to the graph, since it has degree at most 5 and we have 6 colors at our disposal, we can assign v a color that is different from its neighbors. Hence G is 6 colorable.

IV. The 5-color theorem: For any planar graph G, the vertices of G can be properly colored with at most 5 colors.

A. The beginning of the proof is virtually the same as the beginning of the proof of the 6-color theorem. (See outline points A through D above, replacing the number 6 with the number 5.)

B. Bringing v back to the graph, if the number of colors used by the neighbors of v is less than 5, then with 5 colors at our disposal, we can assign v a color that is different from its neighbors, which would show that G is 5 colorable.

C. Hence it remains to consider the case where v has 5 neighbors, but none of them were assigned the same color in the proper coloring of $G - v$. We call its neighbors $v_1, v_2, \ldots,$ v_5 (listed clockwise around v) and suppose that in the proper coloring of $G - v$, they were given the colors red, yellow, green, blue, and purple, respectively.

D. Now suppose we temporarily ignore all edges of G, except for the ones connecting red vertices with green vertices.

   1. If vertices v_1 and v_3 are in different connected components, then in the connected component containing v_1, we can swap the colors red and green and then bring back all the edges of G so that $G - v$ is still properly colored. But now v_1 and v_3 are both green. Thus we can assign v the color red, and we have properly colored G using at most 5 colors.

   2. If vertices v_1 and v_3 are in the same connected component, then there is a fence that surrounds v_2 using v, v_1, v_3, and possibly other red and green vertices, as pictured below.

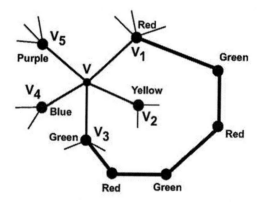

E. Since v_2 is surrounded by a red-green fence and G is planar, there is no way for v_4 to reach v_2 by a blue-yellow path. Thus we can interchange the colors of blue and yellow on the connected component of G containing v_4 that uses only edges that connect blue and yellow vertices. Here, v_4 and v_2 will both be yellow, so we can assign v the color blue, and we have properly colored G with at most 5 colors.

V. The 4-color theorem.

    A. Although the 4-color problem was introduced to the mathematics community in 1852, it remained an open question until it was proved in 1977 by Wolfgang Haken and Kenneth Appel.

    B. Their proof required the construction of a set of over 1000 different graphs, with a computer program checking the logic for each of these cases.

VI. The 4-color theorem can be generalized to other surfaces, such as globes or donuts.

VII. How many different ways can you properly color a graph?

    A. For any graph with n vertices, the number of proper colorings using at most k colors is an nth-degree polynomial with variable k called the chromatic polynomial of G.

    B. The leading coefficient is always 1, and the next term is the negative of the number of edges in G.

    C. The chromatic number is the smallest positive integer z for which $f(z) > 0$, and $f(-1)$ tells you the number of ways you can orient the edges so there are no directed cycles.

    D. A greedy algorithm can tell whether a graph is 2 colorable—also known as bipartite—but a \$1 million prize awaits whoever can discover an efficient algorithm for determining whether any given planar graph is 3 colorable.

Suggested Reading:

Chartrand, *Introductory Graph Theory*, sec. 9.

Lovász, Pelikán, and Vesztergombi, *Discrete Mathematics*, chap. 13.

Rosen, *Discrete Mathematics and Its Applications*, chap. 8.

Scheinerman, *Mathematics: A Discrete Introduction*, secs. 51–52.

West, *Introduction to Graph Theory*, chaps. 5–6.

Wilson, *Four Colors Suffice*.

Questions to Consider:

1. Explain why the complete graph K_n has chromatic number n. If we remove a single edge from K_n, will it have chromatic number $n - 1$?

2. Prove that every tree with $n \geq 2$ vertices has a chromatic number of 2. (Hint: Use a proof by induction on the number of vertices.)

3. Suppose you have m colors at your disposal. Show that the number of ways to properly color a tree with $n \geq 1$ vertices is $m(m-1)^{n-1}$. (Again, try a proof by induction.)

4. We showed that every planar graph has at least 1 vertex of degree 5 or less. Why must, in fact, every planar graph with at least 2 vertices contain at least 2 vertices with degree 5 or less?

5. The planar graph shown below has an interesting property. Can you see what it is? It is a counterexample to a statement that, if it had been true, would have led to a much simpler proof of the 5-color theorem (and the 4-color theorem).

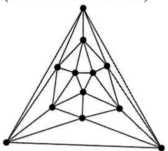

6. A math department plans to offer 7 discrete math courses next semester, namely: Abstract Algebra (A), Combinatorics (C), Data Structures (D), Graph Theory (G), Number Theory (N), Probability (P), and Statistics (S). The math majors and the courses they plan to take are as follows.

Archimedes: A, C, D

Bézout: C, G, S

Carmichael: G, N

Dijkstra: C, D

Euler: D, N

Fermat: C, G

Gauss: N, P

Hardy: G, D

Isaac: A, C

Jacoby: A, C, S

Kuratowski: P, S

Lucas: A, P

How many time periods are needed for these 7 courses? (Hint: This is a graph-coloring problem in disguise.)

Lecture Twenty-Two—Transcript
Coloring Graphs and Maps

In our last lecture, we discussed planar graphs, which can be drawn in the plane with no edges crossing. In this lecture, we'll talk about coloring graphs and coloring maps for which planar graphs will play an important role.

Given a graph G, a coloring of G is obtained by assigning a color to every vertex where repetition is allowed. It's called a "proper coloring" if no adjacent vertices have the same color. For example, this graph here has been properly colored since no adjacent vertices have the same color. We say that a graph is "k colorable" if it can be properly colored using at most k colors. Thus, the graph in our example is 4 colorable, since it can be properly colored with 4 colors. It's also 3 colorable, since we can also do it with 3 colors, like this. Is it 2 colorable? No, because the triangle on top would require that vertices 1, 2, and 5 must be given different colors, so the graph is definitely not 2 colorable.

The smallest number k for which a graph is k colorable is called the "chromatic number" of the graph. Isn't that a colorful name, the chromatic number of the graph? For example, our last graph has a chromatic number of 3, because we can properly color it with 3 colors and not 2. The complete graph K_n has a chromatic number of n, since every vertex must be given a different color. Take a look at this map of the continental USA. You'll notice that in this map, every state is assigned 1 of 4 colors and no 2 adjacent states are given the same color. We say that this map has been properly colored.

Some questions: First of all, can we properly color the states with just 3 colors? We saw [that we were] able to do it with 4; can we do it with 3? The answer is no, and we'll prove that later. Next, can every map be properly colored with just 4 colors? Here the answer is yes. This question—called the 4-color question—has a long history, and we'll say a few words about it after establishing some ground rules of our map. First assumption: Every state is a connected region. A state like Michigan that has two parts to it, that would have to be considered as two separate states. In our coloring, we were able to give both parts of Michigan the same color, but that is not required by our rules. Second: Adjacent states have at least an edge in common. They can't just have a point in common. Their border must contain an edge somehow. Thus, on our map, Arizona is not considered to be adjacent to Colorado, and it would be legal to give Arizona and Colorado the same color. That would be OK; likewise with Utah and New Mexico. This assumption is needed to keep the problem interesting. Otherwise, for this map of Pizzalvania, we would need at least 8 different colors to properly color this map because if everything there was considered to be adjacent, you'd need 8 colors. But by our rules, it can be properly colored with just two colors—plain and pepperoni.

Let me give you a brief history of the 4-color theorem. The 4-color theorem was brought to the attention of the mathematics community in 1852, when a student showed the problem to a prominent logician, Augustus De Morgan; De Morgan circulated the problem to a wider mathematics community. In 1879, Alfred Kempe published a proof, but 11 years later, someone noticed a flaw in his logic. Kempe's logic allowed one to conclude that any map could be properly colored with just 5 colors, but the argument did not extend to 4 colors. The problem became one of the most famous unsolved problems in mathematics, until it was finally proved by mathematicians Kenneth Appel and Wolfgang Haken in 1977, where it became one of the most controversial problems in mathematics. We'll have more to say about their proof later in this lecture.

In this lecture, we'll give a proof of the 5-color theorem and give some background on how the 4-color theorem was proved. First, let's answer the question: Can we properly color the continental US map using just 3 colors? Earlier, I said no, and here's why: Let's focus on the state of Nevada. Let's try to color everything with just 3 colors, and we'll give Nevada the color of yellow. Next to it, California has to have a different color; let's give it red. Oregon has to have a color that's different from California or Nevada; let's give it green. Next we go over to Idaho; now we don't want to introduce a fourth color, but it can't be yellow or green, so we make it red. Then Utah can't be yellow or red, so we have to make it green. But now look at Arizona; it's adjacent to a state that's red, a state that's yellow, and a state that's green. It has to be given a fourth color. Therefore, just by focusing on those states alone, we see that the US map would require at least 4 colors.

How do we prove that every map can be properly colored with at most 5 colors? It's true of 4, but we'll prove it with 5. Any map with a bunch of states can be represented by a graph, as follows: Inside each state, we place a vertex at its capital. Then we connect two capitals with an edge, where that edge just goes through the two states if their states share a border. This is called the "dual graph" of the map. If here's the map of Pizzalvania, and I've drawn its capital in each of those states, then its dual graph would look like that. Here's a more complicated example. This map here has a dual graph that looks like that. Notice, for example, that region A is adjacent to regions B, and D, and F. The face *a* borders face *b*, face *d*, and face *f*, and when we look at its dual graph, we see that vertex *a* is adjacent to vertex *b*, vertex *d*, and vertex *f*. The dual graph is always planar because—why can't any edges cross? The edge that takes us, say, from *a* to *b* can't cross the edge that goes from *c* to *d* because the edge that goes from *a* to *b* stays entirely in regions A and B, and the edge that goes from *c* to *d* stays entirely in C and D, so they're not going to cross.

Coloring the states of the original map—coloring the faces of the original map—corresponds to coloring the vertices of the dual graph. Since we can turn any map problem into a graph problem, where instead of coloring the faces, I'm coloring the vertices, I'm just going to focus on graph problems. For example, this map here with, let's say, region A colored red, and region B colored green, and so on, and we would simply assign the color red to vertex *a*, and the color green to vertex *b*, and so on. I'll say it again: The dual graph is always planar.

At this point, we're going to focus our attention on coloring the vertices of a planar graph so that no adjacent vertices are assigned the same color, and anything we learn about vertex colorings of planar graphs will tell us information about coloring the faces of any map. Thus, if I want to prove the 5-color theorem for any map, our new goal is to prove this theorem: For any planar graph *G*, the vertices of *G* can be properly colored—that is, so that no adjacent vertices have the same color—using at most 5 colors. Or in other words, every planar graph is 5 colorable. To prove this, we're going to need a lemma. I hear you cry, "What's a lemma?!" A lemma is a theorem or a statement that's going to help us prove a bigger statement. The theorem we're really after is the 5-color theorem, but the following lemma will help us get there.

The lemma says this: Every planar graph G must contain a vertex of degree ≤ 5. Let's prove that. Because it's a proof by contradiction, let's suppose to the contrary that it wasn't true. Then there would have to be a graph G that has n vertices, v_1 through v_n, and e edges, such that there would have to be a graph where every vertex had degree greater than or equal to 6. The degree of $v_i \geq 6$ for all i in this graph.

Certainly, we'll have to have at least 7 vertices in such a graph. But by the handshake theorem, we know that the sum of the degrees of the vertices is always twice the number of edges. On the other hand, in a graph like this, we'd have n vertices, each with a degree at least 6, so that the sum of the degrees of the vertices would have to be at least $6n$. Therefore, $2e$ is greater than or equal to $6n$, and that means that e, the number of edges, is greater than or equal to $3n$—3 times the number of vertices. But $3n$ is bigger than $3n - 6$, and that contradicts the planarity of G—remember, G was supposed to be a planar graph—since a planar graph satisfies $e \leq 3n - 6$. Therefore, every planar graph has to have a vertex of degree less than or equal to 5.

Next, we're going to prove the 6-color theorem; we're not ready for 5 colors just yet, but the 6-color theorem is pretty easy. It says, for any planar graph G, the vertices of G can be properly colored with at most 6 colors. Let's prove this by induction on n, the number of vertices. Base case—I have a bunch of base cases—clearly it's true whenever $n \leq 6$. If you have a graph with 6 or fewer vertices, then you could give each vertex a different color; that's going to be a proper coloring that uses at most 6 colors.

Next we state our induction hypothesis: Assume that the theorem is true for planar graphs with k vertices—that any planar graph with k vertices can be properly colored with at most 6 colors. Our goal is to prove it for planar graphs with $k + 1$ vertices. Let G be a planar graph with $k + 1$ vertices. By our lemma, we know there has to be a vertex v where the degree of v is less than or equal to 5. Let's temporarily remove v and its edges from the graph G. This gives us a new graph that we'll call $G - v$. $G - v$ is still planar—you just removed some edges, so it's not going to suddenly cause edges to cross; the graph is still planar—but now it has k vertices, so we can apply the induction hypothesis, which says that this new graph—$G - v$—can be properly colored with at most 6 colors. Do so—properly color it with 6 colors.

Now bring v back into the graph, so we're back to G again. That vertex v had degree that was at most 5. It had at most 5 neighbors, and since it had at most 5 neighbors, we can assign v a sixth color, a color that wasn't used by any of its neighbors. Now the entire graph G has been colored with at most 6 colors, and that's the proof.

That was the 6-color theorem. Now we're ready for the 5-color theorem. It says: For any planar graph G, the vertices of G can be properly colored with at most 5 colors. The beginning of the proof goes exactly the same as the 6-color theorem. We do our base case, we state our induction hypothesis—assume that it's true for any planar graph with at most k vertices, that it can be properly 5 colored. Our goal is to prove it for planar graphs with $k + 1$ vertices. Let G be a planar graph with $k + 1$ vertices; by our lemma, there's a vertex v whose degree is less than or equal to 5. Just like before, we temporarily remove v and its edges from G, giving us the graph $G - v$. Here's where things change. Since $G - v$ is still planar and has k vertices, then by the induction hypothesis, we can properly color $G - v$ with at most 5 colors this time.

Let's get some easy cases out of the way. If v has at most 4 neighbors, then we're done because then we can assign v a fifth color that's different from any of its neighbors, just like in the proof of the 6-color theorem. We'll assume then that v, the vertex we used, really had 5 neighbors. If in the proper coloring of $G - v$ any of those 5 neighbors were given the same color, then there'd be at most 4 different colors among these neighbors. If that's the case, then we can assign v a new color. Here we would let v be green, and we would have now done it with at most 5 colors. Therefore, the only situation we have to worry about is when v has 5 neighbors—let's call them v_1 through v_5—and in the proper coloring of $G - v$, they've all been assigned 5 different colors. Let's call those colors red, yellow, green, blue, and purple, as shown in our figure—in that order, clockwise, around v.

Next, here's the idea: We would like to change v_1 from red to green. If we can get away with that, then we can assign v the color red—because it will have 2 green neighbors—and we'd be done. What's stopping us? Why don't we change v_1 from red to green? The problem is that v_1 might already have some green neighbors. If it didn't, we'd be done; we'd be happy—mission accomplished. But let's say it has some green neighbors. What do you do to those neighbors? You turn them red, right? I know what you're thinking: These might be adjacent to some other red vertices, so turn them green. I know, you're saying that those might be adjacent to some other neighbors; when does the madness stop?

Here's the way I want you to think about it: Imagine I have with me some red-green glasses that only allow me to see vertices that are colored red or green, and I'm going to look at v_1 here. I'm going to look at every vertex that I can reach using only red and green vertices along the way. You can think of this connected component that's connected to v_1 that only uses red and green vertices. If this red-green component doesn't reach vertex v_3, then I'm happy, because what I'll do is, on that red-green component attached to v_1, I'll just turn all my reds into greens and all my greens into reds, and I'll still have a proper component, but now, v_1 would be green instead of red, so I'll be happy.

If that's the case, if that red-green component doesn't include v_3, then we're done. The only situation I have to worry about now is when vertex v is adjacent to 5 different vertices, given 5 different colors, where v_1 is red, v_3 is green, and there exists a red-green path that goes from v_1 to v_3. I've drawn it here; it surrounds the vertex v_2, you'll notice, as we do this. Now, what do we do in this situation? We take v_4 and we switch it from blue to yellow, with the usual chain reaction. This time, I pull out my blue-yellow glasses, and any blue and yellow vertices that are connected on that v_4 component, using only blue and yellow vertices, I'm going to turn everything that's blue into yellow and yellow into blue. Can that component somehow reach v_2? It can't because v_2 is surrounded by this fence, this electric fence of red and green vertices. It can't be penetrated by a blue-yellow chain because none of the vertices surrounding v_2 are blue and yellow, and it can't cross the fence because the graph is planar. What does that mean? That means that we can turn v_4 yellow; now v is adjacent to two yellow vertices. I can color v blue, and we're done.

That's the proof of the 5-color theorem. In his paper, Kempe tried to push this induction argument. This was essentially the induction argument that Kempe used. He tried to extend that induction argument; just as we went from the 6-color theorem to the 5-color theorem, he wanted to do this for the 4-color theorem. His article was published in 1879, but 11 years later, a subtle error was found in his argument, and he was unable to fix the proof. It would take nearly 100 years from the publication of Kempe's paper, until two mathematically trained computer scientists, Kenneth Appel and Wolfgang Haken, were able to prove the 4-color theorem. But it required the construction of a set of over 1000 different graphs and having a computer program check the logic for each of these cases.

The result was controversial for two reasons. [First,] mathematicians were uncomfortable with trusting the computer to provide much of the reasoning. The computer had never been used [before] to the extent that it was in this proof. As far as that issue goes right now, through other independent verifications, the math community now accepts the truth of the theorem. Other people have written similar programs and still used a computer, but they felt that the theorem has been independently verified. The second controversial aspect is: What does it mean to prove a theorem? Is it merely verifying whether a statement is true or false? Or is a proof a human activity that provides people with deeper understanding of the problem? This computer proof certainly didn't accomplish that. I will say, though, that the mathematics community still holds hope that some day a simpler proof will be found.

Surprisingly, the 4-color theorem can be generalized to other surfaces besides the plane. For example, any map drawn on a sphere, like a globe, can be transformed to a map on the plane. Basically, you take a beam of light at the North Pole, and at every point on the globe, that becomes a point on the plane. As a result of that, you can show that any globe can be properly colored with just 4 colors. But the surface of, say, a doughnut, which mathematicians call a "torus," is fundamentally different from a sphere. It's been shown that any map on a torus can be properly colored with just 7 colors, and the surface of a 2-holed doughnut can be properly colored with 8 colors. In general, it's been proved, and without computers, that a map on the surface of a doughnut with g holes in it, where g is a positive number, is always k colorable, where k is the largest integer less than or equal to this number: $\dfrac{7+\sqrt{1+48g}}{2}$, of course. The proof of this theorem requires that the surface have at least 1 hole in it, but what's kind of cool is that the formula still works for the no-hole situation, for the sphere, since when g is 0, the formula gives us $\dfrac{7+\sqrt{1}}{2}$, In other words, 4. It predicts the 4-color theorem even though the proof of it isn't valid for that situation.

Coloring problems arise in more situations than you might think. For instance, if you play the game Sudoku—who doesn't?—you're essentially trying to properly color a graph with 81 vertices, where 2 vertices are adjacent if they are in the same row, or the same column, or the same box of 9. In the game of Sudoku, some of the vertices have already been colored. They've been given a number between 1 and 9, and you have to find the one way to color the rest of them. You have to fill out the box in such a way that no number appears twice in the same row, the same column, or the same box of 9. Graph coloring problems arise also in assigning schedules, such as trying to assign meeting times for various committees in such a way that if two committees have a common member, then they have to meet at different times. The synchronization of traffic signals can also be modeled using graph coloring, too.

Sometimes we're interested in counting the number of different ways you can properly color a graph when you have k different colors to choose from. For example, the path graph of length n can be colored $k(k-1)^{n-1}$ ways. Why is that? If you have k colors, how many choices do you have for vertex 1? [You have] k choices. How many for vertex 2? Now that you had k choices for the first one, you have $k-1$ choices for the second because it can't be the same color as vertex 1. How about vertex 3? That also has $k-1$ choices because it can't be the same as vertex 2, and so on, and so on, and so on. [For] the first vertex, you have k choices, and every vertex after that you have $k-1$ choices, so the number of proper colorings, k colorings, of the path graph of length n is $k(k-1)^{n-1}$.

In fact, the same is true for any tree—not just the path graph—but for any tree with n vertices. Notice, by the way, that $k(k-1)^{n-1}$ is an nth-degree polynomial. It's a polynomial in k with degree n. As it turns out, for any graph with n vertices, the number of proper colorings using at most k colors is always an nth-degree polynomial with variable k. It's called the "chromatic polynomial of G," and it can be computed by a recursion and it has lots of nice properties. For example, it can be shown that the cycle graph C_5, pictured here, has chromatic polynomial $f(z) = (z-1^5) - (z-1)$, which expands out to $z^5 - 5z^4 + 10z^3 - 10z^2 + 4z$. As in this example, notice that the leading coefficient is 1; that's always true. The next term is the negative of the number of edges. The number of edges in C_5 is 5, and we've got a $-5z^4$ term. It's an alternating polynomial that goes positive, negative, positive, negative, positive, negative; you're always going to have that in your chromatic polynomial. The chromatic number is the smallest positive integer z for which $f(z) > 0$. If you think of the definition of chromatic polynomial, that makes sense.

But [consider] this, which is really cool and doesn't make much sense, is that $f(-1)$ tells you the number of ways you can orient the edges so there are no directed cycles. It's kind of like a tournament. How many ways can you orient the edges in such a way that there is not a directed cycle in the graph? If we plug in various values, we see that $f(0)$, $f(1)$, and $f(2)$ all evaluate to 0, so there's no way to color this graph properly with 0, 1, or 2 colors. [Next,] $f(3)$ is 30, which means that there are 30 ways to properly color this graph with 3 colors—let's say red, white, and blue. And $f(-1)$ is -30. What that -30 tells you is that there are 30 ways to orient the edges on C_5 in such a way that you don't get a directed cycle. Now C_5 looks like a cycle. How would you get a directed cycle? Only if all the edges were pointing clockwise or all the edges were pointing counterclockwise. There are 2 ways that create a cycle, and then there are $2^5 - 2$ ways—2 choices, 2 choices, 2 choices—for each of the edges; there are 32 ways of orienting the edges, 2 of which are bad, therefore, 30 of which are good.

Given a graph, it's easy to tell whether it's 2 colorable. By the way, it's also called "bipartite," since they partition the vertices into 2 parts—the blue ones and the red ones. You can tell if a graph is 2 colorable just by proceeding in a greedy way. Take any vertex, color it blue, make its neighbors red, make their neighbors blue, make its neighbors red, and keep on doing that until you've assigned a color to every vertex. If no 2 adjacent vertices have the same color, then you're 2 colorable. If not, you're not 2 colorable. But suppose we ask if that can be done with 3 colors? Then, for some graphs, this problem can be very hard. For example, although it's easy to prove that the United States graph is not 3 colorable, suppose you were given a graph that looks like this. Then the problem could be much harder. In fact, this kind of problem is so hard that if you could find an efficient algorithm to determine if a large arbitrary plane or graph could be properly colored using just 3 colors, then you would actually win $1 million and worldwide fame. We'll learn more about these kinds of problems in our next lecture on algorithms and complexity.

Lecture Twenty-Three
Shortest Paths and Algorithm Complexity

Scope:

In this lecture, we describe and analyze Dijkstra's algorithm for solving the shortest path problem. An algorithm is a systematic method for solving a problem, and we say that this algorithm is efficient because the time required to solve such a problem is at most a polynomial function of n, where n is the number of vertices. By contrast, other problems are not known to have an efficient solution. This leads to a discussion of the complexity classes P and NP as well as the most famous unsolved problem in theoretical computer science, with a $1 million bounty on its head.

Outline

I. The shortest path problem can be solved efficiently using Dijkstra's algorithm.

   A. Given a graph where every edge has a nonnegative weight, we seek to find the shortest path from some vertex A to another vertex B.

   B. We will solve this using Dijkstra's algorithm, which will find the shortest path from A to all vertices in G. (We shall refer to vertices as "nodes" for this algorithm.) The weight of the edge connecting nodes x and y is $w_{xy} \geq 0$. At the end of the algorithm, we will know $C(x)$, the cost of the shortest path from A to x, along with the parent node of x on the shortest path from A to x.

   C. Dijkstra's algorithm.

      1. Step 0. Temporarily assign $C(A) = 0$ and $C(x) = \infty$ for all other x's.

      2. Step 1. Find the node with the smallest temporary value of $C(x)$. (If there are no temporary nodes or if $C(x) = \infty$, then stop.) Node x is now labeled as permanent.

      3. Step 2. For each temporarily labeled node that is adjacent to x, make the following comparison: If $C(x) + w_{xy} < C(y)$, then $C(y)$ is changed to $C(x) + w_{xy}$, and y is assigned to have parent x.

      4. Step 3. Return to step 1.

D. For example, suppose Dijkstra's algorithm is given a graph like this.

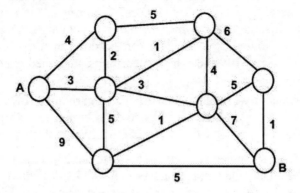

E. At the conclusion of the algorithm, the graph will look like this, where the number written inside of node x is $C(x)$. The bold edges form a tree of shortest paths and connect each edge to its parent node. To find the shortest path from A to x, simply follow the unique bold path from A to x. The shortest path from A to B has total cost 11.

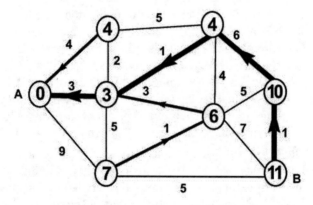

II. A whole class of problems has efficient algorithms.

   A. Given a problem of size n, an algorithm with run time $O(n^k)$ for some k is called a polynomial-time algorithm. These algorithms are efficient.

   B. The computational complexity of a problem is the run time of the fastest algorithm for solving that problem.

   C. We look at some problems that have efficient algorithms.

III. For many other problems, no efficient algorithm is known.

    A. For example, if G has n vertices, then to determine if it is 3 colorable, we could try all possible colorings, but the time to do that is $O(3^n)$, which is not polynomial. Likewise, the Hamiltonian path problem can be done in time $O(n!)$, but that is even worse. These algorithms are called exponential time algorithms.

    B. In fact, if we could find an efficient algorithm to solve any one of these hard problems, it could be turned into an efficient algorithm to solve thousands of other hard problems.

IV. Computer scientists have defined 2 complexity classes, called P and NP. The complexity class P is the set of decision problems that can be solved in polynomial time. (A decision problem is a problem with a yes or no answer.) Some examples include: Is G Eulerian? Is G 2 colorable? Does G have a path from A to B with cost below 100?

    A. The complexity class NP is the set of decision problems where a yes answer can be verified in polynomial time. NP stands for nondeterministic polynomial.

        1. NP includes all problems in P, like the ones listed above.

        2. NP also includes "harder" problems: Does G have a Hamiltonian path? Is G 3 colorable? Is there a Hamiltonian cycle with total cost below 100? These are examples of NP-complete problems, where it has been shown that if any of these problems has a polynomial time solution, then every problem in NP would have a polynomial time solution. This would imply that P = NP.

    B. Does P = NP? Most computer scientists do not think so, but nobody has been able to prove it (or find an efficient algorithm for any of the NP-complete problems). The Clay Mathematical Institute has offered a $1 million prize for anyone who discovers and publishes such a proof or algorithm.

Suggested Reading:

Garey and Johnson, *Computers and Intractability*.

West, *Introduction to Graph Theory*, app. B.

Wilf, *Algorithms and Complexity*.

Questions to Consider:

1. Using Dijkstra's algorithm, find a tree of shortest path from vertex A to all other vertices. In particular, what is the cost of the shortest path from A to B?

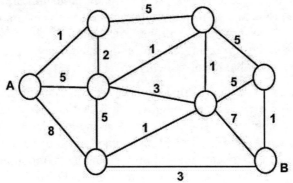

2. We noted how Dijkstra's algorithm can be used to determine whether a graph is connected. Suppose we have a connected graph. Provide an efficient way to determine whether it contains a cycle.

3. Which of these problems belong to the complexity class NP? (In other words, which of these problems are decision problems where a yes answer has a simple verification?)

    a. Does a graph contain a path that goes through at least half of the vertices?

    b. Does an integer n contain a divisor d where $1 < d < n$?

    c. Given a list of positive and negative integers, is there a subset of these integers that sums to 0?

    d. Given a list of positive and negative integers, do all subsets of these integers have a nonzero sum?

    e. Does a graph have a perfect matching (that is, it is possible to find a collection of edges in the graph so that every vertex is incident to exactly 1 edge of the collection)?

    f. Find the longest path in a weighted graph.

Lecture Twenty-Three—Transcript
Shortest Paths and Algorithm Complexity

In this lecture, we examine more problems that can be described by graph theory, including the shortest-path problem, the traveling salesman problem, and the Hamiltonian cycle problem. As we'll see, some of these problems can be solved efficiently, while other similar-sounding problems are so hard that nobody's been able to find a fast algorithm to solve them.

What's an "algorithm"? An algorithm is a systematic method for solving a problem. Its only requirement is that it solves the problem in a finite number of steps. We've encountered algorithms in this course, such as the seed-planting method for raising numbers to powers and the greedy algorithm for finding a minimum-weight spanning tree. But greed is not always good. For example, in this simple shortest-path problem—find the shortest path from vertex 1 to vertex 4—the cost of the shortest path from 1 to 4 is 7. We go from 1 to 3 to 4, which has a total cost of $2 + 5 = 7$. But if instead you'd been greedy, and you said, "What should that first step be? Should I take a step of weight 1 or a step of weight 2?" If you took that step of weight 1, you would have wound up with a cost of 11, which would have been worse than 7, so the greedy algorithm doesn't work in the shortest-path problem.

That was a simple problem, but what would you do to find a shortest path in a graph like this? Or a graph like this, like your GPS tries to do? Here's a more complicated shortest-path problem, although it's still a very, very small problem. People routinely solve shortest-path problems with thousands if not millions of vertices and edges in the graph. Here's a more complicated one: Our goal is to find the shortest path from the vertex labeled a to the vertex labeled b. In the process, in the algorithm that we're going to come up with, we're not only going to find the shortest path from a to b, [but] we're going to find the shortest path from vertex a to every other vertex in the graph. Take a moment; go ahead and pause if you want to see if you can find the shortest path from a to b in this graph. I'll wait. The algorithm that we're going to use is called Dijkstra's algorithm. What's really cool about Dijkstra is that his name has a consecutive I-J-K in it—at least, I think that's kind of neat. Here's the algorithm in front of you. We'll go through it step by step as we need it, starting with step 0, which is: Temporarily assign $C(a)$ to be 0—the cost of vertex a to be 0—and the cost of everything else to be infinite. Here's our graph. $C(x)$ represents the current cost of getting to node x—that's what $C(x)$ gives you. None of these costs [is] permanent yet.

Step 1: Find the node x—and I use the words "node" and "vertex" interchangeably—with the smallest temporary value of $C(x)$. If there are no temporary nodes or if $C(x)$ is infinity, then you're done; the algorithm stops. Node x is now labeled as permanent. That means $C(x)$ and the parent of x will not change again. Let's see what that means in terms of this graph. We find the temporary node that's got the smallest label—that's vertex a; it's got a cost of 0. We label that as permanent; that 0 isn't going to change.

Step 2: For every temporarily labeled vertex y that's adjacent to x—in this case, x is vertex a—make the following comparison: If the cost of x plus the cost of going from x to y is less than the cost of y, then we change things. What do we change? The cost of y is changed to that smaller number—the cost of getting to x plus the weight of the edge from x to y. And we assign y to have a parent of x—and I'll show you what that means in this graph. Our x here is vertex a, and we look at the three edges that come out of it that have costs 4, 3, and 9. I look at $0 + 4$ and I compare that with infinity. Since 4 is much less than infinity, we change that infinity to a 4, and we point back to vertex 0, saying, that's the vertex that made me 4. Then we look at the next edges, 3 and 9. The edge with 3, we see $0 + 3$ is less than infinity; $0 + 9$ is less than infinity, so we change those infinities to 3s and 9s, and they point back to 0, saying that's what gave me my new cost.

Step 3: We return to step 1. We find the node with the smallest temporary value. I see 4, 3, 9, and a bunch of infinities. The smallest number out there that's temporary is the 3. We make that permanent. That 3 isn't going to change its parent, pointing back to the 0. That's not going to change. We look at all the edges leaving 3 that go to other temporary vertices. Here I see 3 and I see the edge with a weight of 2, and $3 + 2 = 5$. How does that compare with 4? The 4 is fine, thank you, just being 4. It doesn't want to change to 5, so we move on: $3 + 1 = 4$—that's better than infinity, so we change that infinity to a 4 and we point back; $3 + 3 = 6$—that's better than infinity; $3 + 5 = 8$. Look what happens here; 8 is less than 9, so we're going to change that 9 to an 8 and we're going to point back—

instead of pointing back to 0—we're going to point back to the 3, saying, yes, that's the vertex that made me 8.

Now we go and look for the cheapest vertex—the temporary vertex with the smallest weight. There's a tie; there's a 4 and a 4. Dijkstra's algorithm says you can choose either one with a tie. We'll choose this one; we make that permanent. There's only one edge that goes to another temporary vertex; that's the 5, but $4 + 5$ is bigger than 4, so we move on. The next vertex is 4, and so we make that permanent, and we look at the edges that go to other temporary places. [That's] $4 + 4$ and $4 + 6$; the $4 + 6$, that beats infinity, so the infinity becomes a 10 and points back. The $4 + 4 = 8$, but that's worse than 6. And the algorithm continues in similar fashion.

What do we do? We find the cheapest vertex. The cheapest temporary vertex is 6; we make that permanent. We look at the edges that go out to other temporary vertices: $6 + 5 = 11$—no, thank you, says the 10; $6 + 7 = 13$—that beats infinity, so that becomes a 13; $6 + 1 = 7$, so that's better than the 8, so we change that 8 to a 7 and point back to the 6. The next cheapest one is the 7. We see that $7 + 5 = 12$; that beats 13. Notice that even though we've reached vertex b, even though that was our goal, we can't stop the algorithm now because that 12 isn't permanent yet. There's still a possibility that it's going to change. We go to 10, that's the next cheapest temporary edge and we look at its vertex. Look at that 1; $10 + 1 = 11$—that's less than 12, so that 12 becomes an 11. Finally, we go to the 11, we make it permanent, and the algorithm stops.

By the way, did you find a shortest path that had a total cost of 11? What is the shortest path? Right now, we have found the shortest path not just from a to b, but we have an entire tree of shortest paths from node a to all other nodes in the graph. If you just want to find the shortest path from a to b, you just start at b and you backtrack to the vertex that gave you the last cost. Here we have 11 points to 10, and 10 points to the 4, and 4 points to the 3, 3 points to the 0— there's your shortest path from node a to node b.

You may ask how fast is Dijkstra's algorithm? Suppose G has n vertices and m edges. Let's analyze this algorithm. Step 0 has time n—that is, step 0 was the one where we assigned 0 to node a and infinity to everything else. We've got to do one thing to each of the n vertices, so it has time n. Step 1 of finding the cheapest temporarily labeled vertex, that's called "at most n times." When you're looking on your list of all the cheapest vertices, that takes you at most n steps. Step 1, the total amount of time that it's going to be used is going to be at most $n \times n$, at most n^2. I'm being very conservative here. Step 2 is basically looking at each edge once a vertex becomes permanent, so each edge is going to be examined essentially twice. Only one of those times are you really going to use it. You'll examine it at most twice. This has a time of at most $2 \times m$, because I've got m edges [and] each edge gets used at most twice.

Roughly speaking, if our graph has n nodes and m edges, then Dijkstra's algorithm takes no worse than about $n^2 + 2m$ steps. Since m is less than n^2, this is no worse than $3n^2$ steps. Computer scientists say that this algorithm is on the order of n^2. They say it's big $O(n^2)$. What that means is it's on the order of at most n^2 steps times a constant, and you could find a constant out there, like maybe it takes you $10n^2$ steps. We call that big $O(n^2)$. Incidentally, a clever computer scientist can actually do this problem in better than $O(n^2)$ time. They could do it in time like $m \log_2 n$ steps, where m is the number of edges, n is the number of vertices, and that might be substantially less than the order of n^2.

Given a problem of size n, an algorithm with a run time of big $O(n^k)$, for some fixed number k, is called a "polynomial time algorithm." Something that's on the order of n^3, that's a polynomial time algorithm. Order of n^4, that's a polynomial time algorithm, but it's a slower one, where n is the size of your problem. The size of a graph problem is typically like the number of vertices or the number of edges. If the size of your problem was just an integer, like if you were factoring or something, then it's how many bits does it take to represent the integer? If your input was just an integer n, the size of that problem would be like the $\log_2 n$.

Sometimes these algorithms that run in polynomial time are called efficient, or sometimes we just simply say that they are good. We define the computational complexity of a problem to be the run time for the fastest algorithm for solving that problem. That can change over time as people find faster algorithms for doing problems. If we don't know of a polynomial time algorithm, maybe we're just not being clever enough. Is there some way to measure that problem's complexity?

Let me answer that by looking at some examples. First, let's start off with some easy problems. The shortest-path problem we've just seen can be solved by Dijkstra in time on the order of n^2. Since n^2 is a polynomial, then that's considered an easy problem. The question: Is G a connected graph? How could you tell if a graph's connected? I know you can tell just by looking at one, but how does your computer tell? One way is it can run Dijkstra's algorithm starting at some vertex a and finding the cost of the shortest path to every other vertex in your graph. When Dijkstra's algorithm finishes, if there's still any vertices out there with a cost of infinity, then there are no paths that get from a to that vertex, and your graph would not be connected. On the other hand, if every vertex has a finite cost, then you know the graph is connected, because we know that any vertex can reach a, so if I can get from x to a and from a to y, then we know it's possible to get from x to y.

How about the question: Is my graph Eulerian? You remember from Euler's great theorem that if a graph is connected and every vertex has even degree, then the graph's Eulerian. We've just seen that it's easy to tell if a graph is connected, and to see if every vertex has even degree, we just look at every vertex and we count the number of edges that go through it. That can be done very efficiently, so yes, determining if a graph is Eulerian is considered an easy problem.

How about: Is a graph 2 colorable? Can I properly color the vertices of a graph using just 2 colors? As I mentioned in the last lecture, yes, you can do that by a greedy algorithm. You just assign a color to one vertex while its neighbors get the opposite color. All the other neighbors that haven't been touched yet, they get the opposite color, and the opposite color, and a chain reaction occurs, and when you're done, you can check to see if the graph has been properly 2 colored.

Those were some easy problems; now let's look at some hard problems. No efficient algorithms have been found for any of these problems. We know there's an algorithm for finding the shortest path in a graph efficiently, but surprisingly, there is no efficient algorithm known to find the longest path in a graph for any possible graph. I'm allowing my graph here to have positive edges or negative edges. Negative edges can create problems.

Is the graph 3 colorable? That is, is there a proper coloring on your graph that can use at most 3 colors? Does the graph have a Hamiltonian path? That is, is there a path that goes through every vertex? These are questions that we don't have efficient answers for. Does the graph have a Hamiltonian cycle? [That's] just as hard.

[Here's] a problem we'll talk more about, the traveling salesman problem; that is, find a Hamiltonian cycle in a graph with weights on the edges so that the sum of the weights is as small as possible. If G is a graph with n vertices, let's look at the 3-colorable problem. If I want to determine if it's 3 colorable, then one algorithm—an actual algorithm for the 3-colorable problem—is: Try all possible colorings. How many colorings, whether they're proper or not, can be given to a graph with n vertices? You've got 3 colors for the first vertex, 3 colors for the second, 3 colors for the third, and so on. There are 3^n ways of doing it. For each of those 3^n ways, you could check to see whether your coloring is proper. To do that, that's going to require on the order of 3^n steps, and that is not polynomial. Don't get 3^n confused with n^3, which is polynomial.

Likewise, the Hamiltonian path problem can be done in time on the $O(n!)$ steps. Just look at every possible circuit that goes through your graph, or look at every possible arrangement of your vertices 1 through n—and there are $n!$ of those—and for each of those say: Is this a Hamiltonian path? Nope, yep, no, nope, there's no edge here. Is this a Hamiltonian path? Just try that on each of them, and again, that will take you time $O(n!)$, but that's even worse than 3^n. These algorithms are called "exponential time algorithms."

By the way, you might say, I see why 3^n is exponential; is $n!$ really exponential? Yes it is, and one way of seeing that is to use something called Stirling's approximation, which says that $n!$ is approximately equal to $\left(\dfrac{n}{e}\right)$—that's the 2.718 number—$\left(\dfrac{n}{e}\right)^n \sqrt{2\pi n}$. I just like to show that formula off because I think it's really pretty. When I say "approximate," I mean in a very rigorous way. The ratio of the left side and the right side is 1 as n gets bigger and bigger and bigger; that ratio gets closer and closer to 1.

In fact, if we could find an efficient algorithm to solve any one of these hard problems, then this could be turned into an efficient algorithm to solve thousands of other hard problems. These problems—all the ones I've mentioned to you—are called "NP hard." There is a million-dollar cash prize for anyone who finds an efficient algorithm for any of these problems. Why are these problems so special? It has to do with complexity classes. Computer scientists have defined two complexity classes—actually, they've defined lots of them—but the two biggies are called P and NP. The complexity class P is the set of decision problems that can be solved in polynomial time. A decision problem is simply a question that has a yes or no answer. [That's] a question like: Is G Eulerian—yes or no? Is G 2 colorable—yes or no? Does G have a path from a to b with costs below 100—yes or no? Those are decision problems. Here's a question that's not a decision problem: Find the shortest path from a to b. You can't say yes or no to that. We'll talk about that later, but the others are decision problems, yes or no answers.

The complexity class NP is the set of decision problems where a yes answer can be verified in polynomial time. NP, by the way, stands for "nondeterministic polynomial." That's a mouthful. It doesn't stand for "non-polynomial." What that simply means is a problem where a yes answer can be checked in a polynomial amount of time, polynomial in terms of the size of the problem. The NP problems include all the problems that were in P, like: Is G Eulerian? Is G 2 colorable? Does G have a path from a to b with costs below 100? If the answer is yes, and I give you an Eulerian trail or an Eulerian cycle, you can check that it works. You say, "Let me see. You say it's Eulerian; let me see your solution: yep, yep, yep, yep, yep. That goes through every edge; I'm happy." Is it 2 colorable? If I give you a proper 2-coloring, you can check that no adjacent vertices have the same color, so those can be checked efficiently.

But we can also find efficient solutions—we can also verify—other problems that are hard; that is, here are some other problems that are in the set NP: Does G have a Hamiltonian path? I don't know how to find one efficiently, but if you give me a Hamiltonian path, I can check that it is indeed a Hamiltonian path in an efficient way. I just follow your path, I see that I've contacted every vertex once, I'm happy. Is G 3 colorable? Again, you give me a proper coloring that uses 3 colors, I can check that no adjacent vertices have the same color. Is there a Hamiltonian cycle with total costs below 100? You give me the cycle, I can add up the costs, and check that it's Hamiltonian in a polynomial amount of time.

These last problems are examples of what are called "NP complete" problems, where it's been shown that if any of these problems have a polynomial time solution, then every problem in NP has a polynomial time solution. I'll say that again: NP complete means that if any of these problems have a polynomial time solution, then all the problems in NP would have a polynomial time solution. This would imply that the set NP doesn't merely contain everything in P but is the same as P, that everything could be done efficiently.

Let me give you a sense as to how you could even possibly hope to show that. The hardest problem in NP is called the satisfiability problem, and it goes like this: Given a logical expression, like A or B, and not B or not C, and C or not A, can we assign truth values—true or false—to A, B, and C so that this expression evaluates to true? It's easy to verify that if I say, sure, let A equal false, B equal true, and C equal false, that this expression evaluates to true. That is, each of those individual expressions, A or B, not B or not C, C or not A, those all evaluate to true, and when I hit each of them with "and" and "and," then true, and true, and true is still true. Although it's easy to verify a solution, you might ask: Is there an efficient way to find a solution? We don't know of any, but in 1971, Stephen Cook proved that if we could find an efficient solution to the satisfiability problem, then it could be used to find an efficient solution to any problem in NP; it's a very deep result. That problem is called "NP complete." The satisfiability question was the original NP complete problem, since solving it would completely solve everything in NP.

Then, Professor Richard Karp came along with a list of several other problems in NP, including the Hamiltonian cycle problem. He showed that if you could efficiently solve any of these problems, then you could solve the satisfiability problem. That is, you could turn the satisfiability problem into a Hamiltonian cycle problem in such a way that the Hamiltonian cycle problem's size hasn't grown all that much. Therefore, if you could solve the Hamiltonian cycle problem in an efficient way, then you could solve the satisfiability problem in an efficient way and, therefore, solve all the problems in NP in an efficient way. These problems are also called NP complete. This led to thousands of other problems being classified as NP complete. A polynomial time solution to any of them would imply that P = NP.

Now let's talk about the traveling salesman problem. Given a graph G, with weights on its edges, the traveling salesman problem, abbreviated the TSP, is to find a Hamiltonian cycle in the graph whose weight is as small as possible. For example, starting in Sacramento, fly to each state capital and return home so that your total miles were as small as possible. This problem is not in NP because it's not a decision problem. You could say, "Oh, here's the way to do it." I can verify that you had a Hamiltonian cycle, but I can't verify that it was the smallest one possible. It's not a decision problem; it's not a yes or no question. Nevertheless, if a polynomial time solution could be found for it, it would also imply that P = NP. A problem like this that's not in NP but still would give you efficient solutions to all of NP, those problems are called "NP hard." Actually, everything that's NP complete is NP hard, but there are other problems that aren't in NP that are also NP hard.

Does P = NP? Most computer scientists don't think so, but nobody's been able to prove it or find an efficient algorithm for any of the NP complete problems. There's $1 million prize offered by the Clay Mathematical Institute for a proof or disproof of the conjecture that P $\neq$ NP. A proof or disproof would win you $1 million.

In practice, what do you do if someone asks you to solve an NP hard problem? Do you just throw up your hands and say, "Oh, I've taken this course; I know there are no efficient solutions." No, you just do the best you can. Often, there are efficient algorithms that can guarantee a solution that's within a certain percent of optimality. For example, the minimum-spanning tree algorithm, which can be done efficiently, can actually be adapted to produce a Hamiltonian cycle— a solution to the TSP—that's at most twice as expensive as the minimum-cost Hamiltonian cycle. More sophisticated methods exist that will, with high probability, find a solution to a problem with millions of cities to within 2 to 3 percent of optimality. That's pretty impressive. So long as you don't insist on a perfect solution, you can still do well in practice.

We've seen the graph theory problems can be hard. I want to show you that combinatorics problems can be hard, too. For example, take this problem: How many matches do we have? No, not those matches; I mean—yeah, matches like that, matches in a graph, like the graph $K_{4,4}$ in the stable marriage algorithm, so it's the complete bipartite graph—4 vertices on the left, 4 vertices on the right. How many matches? It's easy to see there are 4! ways because the first vertex can be matched to 4 vertices, the second one can be matched to 3, then to 2, then to 1; no problem. In general, $K_{n,n}$ has $n!$ matches. But what if we throw away a bunch of edges? Then, the same combinatorics problem can get really hard. Although there exists efficient algorithms that can tell us if there's at least one match, the exact number of matches is in a complexity class called "sharp P complete." That "sharp" is both the musical sharp symbol and the symbol for the number sign [#]—how many? The sharp P complexity class are problems where if you could actually count this problem exactly in polynomial time, then you would prove that P = NP, and you'd win $1 million.

Not only can combinatorics be hard, [but] number theory can be hard, too. As we saw, the problem of factoring a large composite number seems to be hard. It's not known whether that problem is NP complete, but the fact that it's hard actually has its advantages. It allows us to create some very secure methods for cryptography. On the other hand, prime detection, determining whether or not a number is prime, is actually easy, and that's a very recent result. It was proved in 2002 by three mathematicians from India who showed that the prime detection problem is in the complexity class P. What's really cool about this is that two of those three mathematicians were undergraduates.

In our final lecture, we'll take a look back, put everything together, glance beyond the bounds of this course, and explore some truly magical applications of discrete mathematics.

Lecture Twenty-Four
The Magic of Discrete Mathematics

Scope:

We take a look back at some common themes of discrete mathematics as well as a look ahead at some topics that you can pursue to build on your solid foundation. We also include some truly magical applications of the material in this course.

Outline

I. There are numerous places where the 3 major fields of discrete mathematics (combinatorics, number theory, and graph theory) overlap.

  A. We saw how proofs, especially proofs by induction, played an important role in all 3 topics and how counting methods were often applied outside of the combinatorics lectures.

  B. We saw how the powers of 2 arise as the solution to counting problems but also provide us with additive building blocks for the integers.

  C. We saw Fibonacci numbers make cameo appearances in all 3 fields.

  D. We were introduced to many mathematicians, but the one we encountered most often was Leonhard Euler. We saw 3 theorems that were named after him: 1 in number theory, 2 in graph theory, and we will soon see 1 in combinatorics.

II. Discrete mathematics is often a prerequisite to many upper-division courses in mathematics and computer science, some of which we highlight here.

  A. Abstract algebra is the language of symmetry, and one of its main topics is group theory. A group is a set that has lots of structure.

  B. In set theory and logic, you learn how sets and logical symbols have an algebra all of their own.

  C. Earlier we encountered binary trees as a means of storing information. In a course on data structures and algorithms, you are exposed to other ways to store data that have nice properties.

D. In a full-length course on combinatorics, you would certainly spend some time learning about generating functions.

E. In a full-length course on number theory, the prime numbers take on different personalities.

F. In a course on graph theory, you would explore more properties of graph coloring.

III. Some magic tricks are based on discrete mathematics.

A. Write down the following 3 numbers: your phone number (P), the number 8, and then $8P$. Add those numbers together. Add the digits of your answer together, resulting in a 2-digit number. Then add the digits of your 2-digit number. You will always get 8. Why? Their sum is $9P + 8$, which is congruent to 9 (mod 8).

B. If 16 cards are placed face down in a 4×4 grid with aces on the diagonal and 4 face-up cards on the spots that are diagonally adjacent to the aces, then after the cards are folded onto 1 spot, all 4 aces will be facing in the opposite direction from the rest of the cards. The secret is based on parity.

C. Using a complete set of dominoes, with 1 domino secretly removed (say the 3-4 domino), ask your volunteer to arrange the dominoes in 1 long line, with the requirement that touching dominoes have matching numbers. Then the endpoints of the domino chain are guaranteed to be 3 and 4. The secret is based on Eulerian paths, where every domino represents an edge of K_7. Every vertex has even degree except vertices 3 and 4.

IV. With magical mathematics—such as that of magicians like Euler and Ramanujan—even after seeing what they accomplished, we are still mystified as to how they did it.

V. My hope is that you now see how *discrete* mathematics can be a source of *continuous* enjoyment. At least that is what I am counting on!

Suggested Reading:

Benjamin and Brown, *Biscuits of Number Theory*.

Benjamin and Quinn, *Proofs That Really Count*.

Bogart, *Introductory Combinatorics*.

Graham, Knuth, and Patashnik, *Concrete Mathematics*.

Niven, Zuckerman, and Montgomery, *An Introduction to the Theory of Numbers*.

West, *Introduction to Graph Theory*.

Questions to Consider:

1. The Fibonacci identity given in the lecture, $\sum_{k=0}^{n} \binom{n}{k} F_k = F_{2n}$, has a nice combinatorial proof using tilings. We do this by first rewriting the identity using "little f" notation: $\sum_{k=0}^{n} \binom{n}{k} f_{k-1} = f_{2n-1}$. The right side counts the ways to tile a board of length $2n - 1$ with squares and dominoes. We claim that the left side does the same. To see this, note that any board of length $2n - 1$ must have at least n tiles—since if it had $n - 1$ tiles, its length would be at most $2(n - 1) = 2n - 2$. To complete the proof, show that the number of tilings with exactly k squares among the first n tiles is $\binom{n}{k} f_{k-1}$.

2. Take any 4-digit number (except for one where all the digits are the same, like 7777). Scramble the digits to create a second 4-digit number. Now subtract the smaller number from the larger. (For example, if your 4-digit number was 2358, and you scrambled them to get 5382, you would now calculate $5382 - 2358$.) Now take the answer to the subtraction problem and sum the digits. If you have a 1-digit number, then stop. If you have a 2-digit number, then sum the digits to obtain a 1-digit number. What number will you always end up with, and why?

3. The domino prediction trick in the lecture used dominoes that had 2 different numbers from the set $\{0, 1, 2, 3, 4, 5, 6\}$. Would the trick have worked if the dominoes came from the set $\{0, 1, 2, 3, 4, 5, 6, 7, 8, 9\}$?

4. Place 5 cards in front of you, from left to right: ace, 2, 3, 4, 5. Place your finger on the ace or the 5, then take 5 steps. At each step, you can move your finger to the left or to the right, as long as you stay on the cards. Now remove the ace and the 5 (since your finger will not be there) and take 5 more steps. What card will you end on? Why does this trick work?

Lecture Twenty-Four—Transcript
The Magic of Discrete Mathematics

Lecture Twenty-Four—we made it! Let's take a look back at the material that we've covered in this course. We've presented this course as three major fields—combinatorics, number theory, and graph theory. But there were numerous places where these fields overlapped. For instance, we saw how proofs—and especially proofs by induction—played an important role in all three topics, and counting methods were applied many times outside the set of combinatorics lectures. We saw my favorite numbers—the Fibonacci numbers—make cameo appearances in all three subjects. They counted the ways to tile a strip with squares and dominoes, the number of perfect matchings in a 2-by-n graph, and they provided us with an upper bound on how long it takes the important Euclidean algorithm to run. I could probably offer an entire course on the magic of Fibonacci numbers that combine and go beyond several aspects of this course. For example, when you combine Fibonacci numbers with binomial coefficients, we can get beautiful identities, like this one, $\sum_{k=0}^{n} \binom{n}{k} F_k = F_{2n}$, which can be proved using induction, the binomial theorem, or combinatorially. Incidentally, if you like the material on combinatorics and combinatorial proofs and you want to see more of them, you might enjoy my book, *Proofs That Really Count*, co-authored with one of my favorite mathematicians, Professor Jennifer Quinn.

We saw how the powers of 2 played an important role throughout this course. They provide us with additive building blocks for the integers. Any number can be represented as the sum of distinct powers of 2 in a unique way. For instance, 83 is $64 + 16 + 2 + 1$. Those are all distinct powers of 2. And yet, a similar result holds for Fibonacci numbers. Any number can be written as the sum of distinct, nonconsecutive Fibonacci numbers in a unique way. For instance, 83 can be expressed as $55 + 21 + 5 + 2$, all of which are distinct, nonconsecutive Fibonacci numbers. This is known as the Zeckendorf representation.

In graph theory, the Fibonacci numbers count the ways that you can choose vertices from a path graph so that no two of them are adjacent. These collections are called "independent sets."

For example, here are the path graphs of lengths 1 to 4 and their independent sets. When N is 1, there are two ways of doing it. When N is 2, there are three ways to do it. When N is 3, there are five ways to do it. When N is 4, there are eight ways: 2, 3, 5, 8; I hope you now appreciate Fibonacci. By the way, when N is greater than or equal to 2, the number of independent sets in a cycle graph of length N is the Nth Lucas number that we also encountered. Notice here, when N is 2, 3, 4, and 5, the number of independent sets in them is 3, 4, 7, and 11, which are Lucas numbers.

We were introduced to many mathematicians, but the one we encountered most often was Leonhard Euler. We saw three theorems that were named after him—one in number theory and two in graph theory. By the end of this lecture, I'll show you another one of his in combinatorics.

What can you do with a course in discrete mathematics? At my school, Harvey Mudd College, discrete mathematics is required of math majors and computer science majors. Students from other majors take it as an elective course. Since it's the first really proof-intensive course, it's a prerequisite for many upper-level courses, like abstract algebra, logic and set theory, data structures and algorithms, and full-length courses in combinatorics, number theory, and graph theory.

Let me say a few words about each of these courses. Abstract algebra is the language of symmetry, and one of its main topics is group theory. A group is a set where the elements can be multiplied together in such a way that the product always stays in the set. Multiplication is associative—that means $(ab)c$ equals $a(bc)$ no matter how you parenthesize. There's a number, which I'll call 1, that acts like the real number 1. That is, when you multiply 1 by something, it doesn't change, and for every number x, we can find another number that kind of acts as a reciprocal, a number y so that xy gives us 1. The positive real numbers form a group, but there are some finite sets that do, too, like the set of numbers 1 through $p - 1$, when p is a prime and multiplication is done mod p.

One great result from group theory is Lagrange's theorem, which says that if G is a group, and H is a subgroup of G—that is, a group that lives inside of that group—then the number of elements in H must divide the number of elements in G. If the size of a group is N, then a consequence of Lagrange's theorem is: For any element x in the group, when you take x^N, you always get the identity element 1. Fermat's theorem and Euler's theorem, which we saw earlier, are in fact, very simple, special cases of these theorems from group theory. Group theory overlaps, by the way, with combinatorics and graph theory, too. For example, we can use group theory to count the number of ways that we could paint a cube with n colors, where 2 cubes are considered to be the same if one cube can be rotated to look like the other. Groups often have beautiful graphical representations that I won't go into here, but I'll show you some pictures.

Let me say a few words about set theory and logic. In set theory—we played around with sets just a little bit in this course—you can prove things like $A \cap (B \cup C) = (A \cap B) \cup (A \cap C)$. You can demonstrate that with a Venn diagram or by various logical arguments. Another nice identity is that if you take the set of points that are not in A, or B, or C, that's equal to the set of points that are not in A, and not in B, and not in C. Just like set theory has some nice laws, like distributive laws, so do the laws of logic. For any truth values A, B, and C, where A, B, and C can be true or false, you can get statements like A and B or $C = A$ and B or A and C. There's a similar law of negation called De Morgan's law. In a sense, we can actually do algebra on logic; this is called Boolean algebra, and it reminds me of a funny cartoon I recently saw. It showed the logician George Boole in a restaurant, and it says, "Boole orders lunch." He's going down the menu and he's saying, "Yes, yes, no, no, yes, yes, yes, no," thinking very discretely.

Here's another course that discrete mathematics is applied to—data structures and algorithms. Earlier, we encountered binary trees as a means of storing information, but there are other ways to store data that have nice properties. For example, we saw binary trees where every vertex had two children, except the leaves at the bottom. There are some trees called 2-3 trees where all the leaves are at the bottom and they're all at the same height or the same depth from the top of the tree. All the leaves are, in a sense, just like all the other leaves. Every vertex above those leaves has degree 2 or 3; that is to say, it has two children or three children.

Another thing one would learn in a course like that are sorting algorithms. What's the fastest way to sort numbers? The obvious ways take about time proportional to n^2. The clever ways are time proportional to $n \log n$. If you were to take a full-length course in combinatorics, you might encounter generating functions. A generating function goes as follows: Suppose you had a sequence of numbers, a_0, a_1, a_2, a_3, and so on, and rather than list them out in one long list with commas separating them, instead, we turn them into a mathematical function called a "generating function." The generating function for that sequence would be called a of x, which would be $a_0 + a_1x + a_2x^2 + a_3x^3$ and so on. We're displaying all the values on sort of a mathematical clothesline where we're looking as if it's like an infinitely long polynomial. Sometimes, this will have a very nice, simple form that reveals a lot of information about your sequence. For example, let's take our favorite sequence, the Fibonacci numbers—1, 1, 2, 3, 5, 8, and so on. That has, as a generating function, $1 + 1x + 2x^2 + 3x^3 + 5x^4 + 8x^5$ and so on. If x is small enough in absolute value, that actually simplifies to the function $\dfrac{1}{1-x-x^2}$. Or you could do polynomial long division and see that that works regardless of what x is.

It's just amazing, that in essence, the entire set of Fibonacci numbers is captured in that one formula, that one function, $\dfrac{1}{1-x-x^2}$. We can derive Binet's formula from this, along with many other properties of the Fibonacci numbers. This, by the way, shows that discrete mathematics and continuous mathematics actually do have a lot to say to each other. The more you know about one side, the more it can help you on the other.

If you were to take a full-blown course in number theory, you'll see that we spend a lot more time with prime numbers—in fact, so much that they start developing their own personality. In my course, I refer to "good primes" and "bad primes." The good primes are the primes that are 1 bigger then a multiple of 4; the bad primes are the ones that are 3 bigger than a multiple of 4, or you could say 1 less then a multiple of 4. The number 2 is the only even prime, so it's a little odd, wouldn't you say?

Anyway, here's one of the classic results in number theory that we spend a bit of time talking about. It's called quadratic reciprocity and it says this: When does a number have a square root mod p? If I give you a number q, can you find a number whose square gives you $q \pmod{p}$? The answer to that—there's really a rather beautiful theorem involving that, called quadratic reciprocity, that says this:

With one sort of exception—with one class of exceptions—q has a square root mod p if and only if p has a square root mod q. This is true whenever p and q are prime numbers, but there's an exception. The only time that doesn't work is when both p and q are bad prime numbers, when they're bad primes—both of them 3 bigger than a multiple of 4—then q has a square root mod p if and only if p doesn't have a square root mod q. As strange as this theorem sounds, it actually has applications, like allowing you to figure out how to flip coins over the telephone in such a way that you can actually trust the person on the other end without really seeing a coin. It's more of a numerical coin.

If you were to take a full-blown course in graph theory, you might encounter coloring problems a little different from what we saw. In this course, we colored faces on a map [and] we colored vertices on a graph. You could also properly color the edges in such a way that two edges that go into the same vertex are not allowed to have the same color. How many colors are you going to need? First, if you look at your graph and you find the vertex that has the biggest degree, let's call that degree delta—big delta [Δ]—then obviously, that vertex alone is going to need Δ different colors, so your graph is going to need at least Δ colors. Vizing's theorem says that the minimum number of colors that you need is either going to be Δ or $\Delta + 1$. It's got to be one or the other, and that's the edge chromatic number of the graph. Given a large graph, even deciding whether the chromatic number—the edge chromatic number—is Δ or $\Delta + 1$, that also turns out to be an NP complete problem.

There are plenty of advantages to learning discrete mathematics if you go on to take other mathematics courses. But let's see some stuff you can appreciate right here, right now. As I said, this lecture is on the magic of discrete mathematics. I want to now show you some magic tricks whose secrets are actually based on discrete mathematics, so the more you understand your discrete math, the better you can understand the magic tricks.

My first trick is one I call the magic of 8. I learned it from the ultimate mathemagician, Martin Gardner. First, I want you to write down a number, it can be a one-digit, a two-digit number; it could be a seven-digit phone number, whatever you're comfortable with. Write that as your first number. Get out a piece of paper. The second number, I want you to write down the number 8 because this is after all, the magic of 8. The third number—you might need a calculator for this—is to take that first number and multiply it by 8. Now you have three numbers. I want you to add those three numbers together, and you'll get some big number. Whatever that big number is, I want you to take the digits of that big number and add them together. If you have a one-digit number now, stop. If you have a two digit number, I want you to sum those two digits and see what answer you get. Because this is the magic of 8, you should have, if we've done all our calculations correctly, the number 8.

How did I do it? Did I have an in-8 sense of things? No, I just knew a little bit of number theory. Here's the secret: The first number, we can call that P; maybe P is your phone number. The second number is 8; the third number is $P \times 8$. When we add those three numbers together, we get $9P + 8$. When I ask you to add the digits, then add the digits again, you know that means we're just working mod 9, and when we put on our mod 9 glasses, $9P + 8$ simply looks like the number 8.

The next trick is one involving cards. I won't need all of these cards; I'll just need some of them. I can put some of the cards—they can come from the top, they can come from the bottom, they can go anywhere in the deck that we want, the middle even. I want 16 cards altogether here. I'll ask you how you want me to fold these cards up. Before I do, here, I'll flip a couple of these cards over, see what we have here: 2, 3, 9, 4, OK—2, 3, 4, 9; that's interesting. Now I'm going to ask you, do you want me to fold from the left, the right, the top, or the bottom? You pick the first one. The top, so I'll take the top and I'll fold it down, just like that. Then, the left? Then, the left again? Sure. And then the bottom, and then the top, and one more, like that. If we've done all of our cutting and folding correctly, we should have the four aces. Isn't that nice?

Some of you may have seen a trick like this before; you're now going to learn the mathematics behind it. It's probably best explained with a visual aide—I brought one here. The first bit of sneakiness is that the four aces start off on the top of the deck, and as I'm putting them down and up, I make sure as I'm randomly putting them down in any which way, that the four aces somehow manage to be on the main diagonal, so the aces should be here. That's step 1. You want to nonchalantly get those aces on the diagonal, this black diagonal. Now I turn four other cards up; almost as an afterthought, we'll turn these four cards up. It's always these four cards. Why? Because the four aces are on the black diagonal, I'm turning the other four black cards up.

Then, we go through our folding procedure, and as we fold, and fold, and fold, we're eventually going to consolidate on one spot. Let's say we end up on this spot here. What can I say about this ace? What's going to happen to this ace? How many steps will it take to go from here to there? It might go over there in one space, but it might also go over there in three spaces, or possibly five spaces, or however many spaces it takes, it has to be an odd number. Why? Because it starts on a black square, and every move that you make as you fold, you move from black to white or white to black—we're using parity here. What can I say about its orientation by the time it gets from this black square, face down? Every time it's on a white square, it's face up. Every time it's on a black square, it's face down. If it ends up here, it's going to end up face up, and so will all the other four aces because they started on black squares. After making an odd number of flips, they'll end up here face up.

What about these other four cards that started on black squares? They'll also take an odd number of steps, but since they started face up, by the time they end up here, they will be face down. Finally, all these white cards, those are all face down. How many steps will they take to get there? Since it goes from white to white, it's necessarily going to take an even number of steps. So if they start face down, then after an even number of steps, they will also be face down. Therefore, when all the cards are on this square, all the aces will be face up, all the non-aces will be face down, and if you ended up, say, all collecting on a black square instead, it will just be the reverse. You can just turn the cards over as you spread them out and that gives you your four-ace surprise.

The next trick uses these dominoes, and I have in my possession a complete set of dominoes. The dominoes have every possible pair on them, so they go from 0 to 6. The 0 is represented by a blank, and I ask my assistant—whoever that may be—to arrange the dominoes on the table in such a way that they must always match as you go from one end to the next. This 3 has to be connected to a 3, this 2 with a 2, and so on. They could turn around the corner if that makes your job easier. Let's see, while we're doing this, here's a quick combinatorics question: How many dominoes should be here? We have 7 possible values, we choose 2 of them so that they're different, so there should

©2009 The Teaching Company.

be $\binom{7}{2}$ possibilities. [Now,] what do we have here? Let's look at the endpoints of our domino. Remember, this is done by a volunteer. They can arrange them however they want as long as they use all of them. Before I started my trick however, I did a little back-of-the-envelope calculation predicting what the endpoint of our path was going to be. We see that we started here with a 3, and we ended here with a 4. You'll see that my prediction was that very result, 3 and 4.

How does that work? What's the secret behind this magic? It's nothing more than graph theory and a little bit of deception on my part. When I told you at the beginning that I had in my possession a complete set of dominoes, that was true. But $\binom{7}{2}$ is 21 dominoes, and I only had 20 of them here on the table. The 21st domino I had in my possession, but it was in my pocket. It was this domino 3:4. Why does that guarantee that we're going to have our endpoints as 3 and 4? Take a look at the graph K7, complete graph with vertices going from 0 to 6 where 0 represents the blank domino. Every edge in the graph represents a domino. For instance, the edge that goes from 2 to 5, that represents the domino that begins with a 2 and ends with a 5.

What can I say about the degree of every vertex? It's the complete graph on 7 vertices. Every vertex is adjacent to all 6 other vertices. It's a connected graph; every vertex has even degree. Euler's graph theorem says that the graph must be Eulerian. But then I took away the domino 3:4. That gets rid of the edge that goes from 3 to 4. As a result, this graph doesn't have every vertex having even degree; 3 and 4 have odd degree. It's no longer Eulerian, but it is still drawable. We know that the only way that it can be drawn is if the endpoints are those points that have odd degree—namely, the 3 and 4, and that's why your prediction is guaranteed. By the way, the trick still works even if we add the dominoes that are matches—the double-5 domino, the double-6 domino, and so on. The trick will still work even if you have them. But instead of having $\binom{7}{2}$ dominoes, you'd have $\left(\!\binom{7}{2}\!\right)$ dominoes, -1, of course.

Now we switch from mathematical magic to magical mathematics. It's been said that there are two kinds of geniuses—the ordinary kinds and the magicians. The ordinary kinds are just like us. We could have figured out what they did if only we were about 10 times as smart. But the magicians, even after seeing what they accomplished, we're still completely mystified as to how they did it. When I think of who in the history of mathematics possessed supernatural qualities, the first two that come to my mind are Euler and Ramanujan. Both of them worked on problems involving integer partitions, which we briefly encountered in Lecture Three on the 12-fold way of combinatorics. It's a topic that spans combinatorics, number theory, and even a little graph theory.

Recall that the partition number $p(n)$ counts the number of ways to allocate n identical pieces of candy into any number of identical bags. More simply, it's the number of ways to write the number n as the sum of smaller numbers where order doesn't matter. For example, $p(1)$ is 1 because I can just write 1 one way. And the number 2, $p(2)$ is 2 because 2 can be written as 2 or as $1 + 1$. [The number] 3 can be written three ways, either as 3, or as $2 + 1$, or as $1 + 1 + 1$. Notice I don't have $1 + 2$ on that list because it's the same as $2 + 1$; order doesn't matter. We see a pattern, right? It's 1, 2, 3—do you think $p(4)$ is 4? Actually, it's 5. But we see another pattern, 1, 2, 3, 5—I'll bet the next one is 8, right? No, $p(5)$ is 7. Wait, I see 2, 3, 5, 7—those are prime numbers; maybe the next one is 11. Sure enough, $p(6)$ is 11. How about $p(7)$; will that be 13? Nope, it's 15. We wouldn't expect the prime numbers to be that well behaved, would we?

As it turns out, there is no exact formula for $p(n)$. But Euler found a recurrence, and it's kind of like the Fibonacci numbers on steroids. Here it is: It starts off like Fibonacci; $p(n)$ is $p(n - 1) + p(n - 2)$. But then we subtract two things: $p(n - 5)$ and $p(n - 7)$. Then we add two things back: $p(n - 12) + p(n - 15)$. Then I subtract two things, and then I add two things, and then I subtract two things, and this goes on forever until we reach 0 or below. If we reach 0, we have p of 0 is 1. If we go negative, p of anything negative is 0. The numbers are added and subtracted, two at a time, and the numbers that we see here are of the form $\pm p(n - k)$, where k is of the form $\dfrac{j(3j \pm 1)}{2}$.

You can use that recurrence to solve for $p(5)$, $p(6)$, $p(7)$ successively and you'll see they match up with the numbers that we saw earlier. There's the formula; there's even a more compact way of writing it using summation notation. It's called Euler's pentagonal number theorem, since numbers of the form $\dfrac{j(3j \pm 1)}{2}$ are called pentagonal numbers, as is illustrated below.

Recall that the Fibonacci numbers have a generating function: $a(x)$ is $1 + 1x + 2x^2 + 3x^3 + 5x^4 + 8x^5$ and so on. We saw that for small values of x, that simplifies to $\dfrac{1}{1 - x - x^2}$, the generating function for partition numbers, where we're using 1, 1, 2, 3, 5, 7, 11, 15, and so on, that also has a nice simplifying generating function, but the denominator is an infinitely long product. It's

$$\frac{1}{(1 - x)(1 - x^2)(1 - x^3)(1 - x^4)(1 - x^5)\ldots}$$ and so on, out for ever.

Because of that, it has no simple closed form, but Hardy and Ramanujan discovered that $p(n)$ has a beautiful asymptotic formula. They showed that $p(n) \cong \dfrac{e^{\pi\sqrt{2n/3}}}{4n\sqrt{3}}$ —go figure! You look at a number like that and it reminds you that even if you live, breathe, and love discrete mathematics, like I do, you can't totally escape the continuous mathematics. Here, even though these are problems about integers, we still see the numbers from calculus and geometry. We see e, π, [and] square roots. The more you know about the one field, discrete mathematics, the more it's going to help you in continuous mathematics and vice versa.

Congratulations, you've just gone through a very rigorous mathematics course—quite possibly the first course you've ever taken where the emphasis was on concepts and problem solving, instead of plugging and chugging through formulas and symbol pushing. You've probably never done so many proofs before either, except perhaps in your high school geometry class.

I didn't expect you to come into this course with a love of doing proofs, but I hope that you have a better appreciation for them now. The rigorous training that you've just had in discrete mathematics and logical thinking skills should serve you well in your daily life, as well as in any future math courses you may choose to take; at least, that's what I'm counting on. Thank you.

Answers to Questions to Consider

Lecture Thirteen

1. Using the prime factorizations of the numbers 2 through 12 and looking at the largest exponent achieved by each prime, we see that the least common multiple of these numbers is $2^3 3^2 5^1 7^1 11^1 = 27,720$.

2. We are looking for the smallest positive integer N for which $N \equiv 3 \pmod{13}$ and $N \equiv 8 \pmod{17}$, which we can solve by the Chinese remainder theorem. Since 13 and 17 are relatively prime, there exist x and y such that $13x + 17y = 1$. Using the Euclidean algorithm, if needed, we find this equation is satisfied by $x = 4$ and $y = -3$. Thus, by the "max + may" formula, $N \equiv (13)(8)(4) + (17)(3)(-3) = 263 \equiv 42 \pmod{221}$. Hence the band has 42 musicians.

3. For this problem, we combine the solution of the last problem, $N \equiv 42 \pmod{221}$, with $N \equiv 1 \pmod 7$. To find x and y such that $221x + 7y = 1$, we can solve (by trial and error or Euclid) and find that this equation is satisfied by $x = 2$ and $y = -63$. Therefore $N \equiv (221)(1)(2) + (7)(42)(-63) = 442 - 18,522 = -18,080 \pmod{1547}$. Adding the smallest multiple of 1547 to $-18,080$ to make it positive, we see that $N = -18,080 + 12(1547) = -18,080 + 18,564 = 484$. It is worth checking that indeed 484 mod 221 = 42 and 484 mod 7 = 1.

4. **a.** With 22 cards, an outshuffle will take the card in position x and move it to position $2x$ mod 21 (when $0 \le x < 21$; the card in position stays in position 21). We can represent this permutation in terms of cycles: (0)(1 2 4 8 16 11) (3 6 12)(5 10 20 19 17 13)(7 14)(9 18 15)(21). So the number of shuffles needed to restore the deck is the least common multiple of $\{1, 6, 3, 6, 3, 2, 3, 1\} = 6$. A quicker solution is to notice that after 6 shuffles, a card in position x will be sent to position $2^6 x = 64x \equiv x \pmod{21}$, so every card will be back to its original position.

b. For a deck of size N to be restored after 4 outshuffles, it must be the case that $2^4 x = 16x \equiv 1x \; (mod \; N-1)$ for every value of x. In particular, when $x = 1$, we must have $16 \equiv 1 \; (\text{mod} \; N-1)$. The largest value of $N-1$ that can do this is 15, and therefore the largest deck that has this property contains exactly 16 cards.

5. This can be solved by the lucky method or the seed planting method. With the lucky method, notice that $3^6 = 729$ is 1 bigger than $728 = 91 \times 8$. Therefore $3^6 \equiv 1 \; (\text{mod} \; 91)$. So by the power rule, $3^{90} = (3^6)^{15} \equiv 1^{15} = 1 \; (\text{mod} \; 91)$. Multiplying both sides by 3 gives us $3^{91} \equiv 3 \; (\text{mod} \; 91)$.

To compute it by seed planting, express $91 = 64 + 16 + 8 + 2 + 1$ as $(101011)_2$. Then by successive squaring of 3, with seeds planted at steps 1, 3, 5, and 6, we get:

Step 1: 3

Step 2: $3^2 = 9$

Step 3: $9^2 \times 3 = 243 \equiv -30 \; (\text{mod} \; 91)$

Step 4: $(-30)^2 = 900 \equiv -10 \; (\text{mod} \; 91)$

Step 5: $(-10)^2 \times 3 = 300 \equiv 27 \; (\text{mod} \; 91)$

Step 6: $(27)^2 \times 3 = 2187 \; (\text{mod} \; 91) = 3$.

Lecture Fourteen

1. The proper divisors of $220 = 2^2 5^1 11$ are 1, 2, 4, 5, 10, 11, 20, 22, 44, 55, and 110—which sum to 284. The proper divisors of $284 = 2^2 71$ are 1, 2, 4, 71, and 142—which sum to 220.

2. Since $2^n - 1$ is prime, we shall denote it by the number p. The divisors of $x = 2^{n-1}p$ can be split into those divisors that do not use p $(1, 2, 4, \ldots, 2^{n-1})$ and those that do use p $(1p, 2p, 4p, \ldots, 2^{n-1}p)$. The first group sums to $2^n - 1$, which equals p. The second group sums to p^2. Therefore the sum of all the divisors is $p^2 + p = p(p + 1) = 2^n p = 2(2^{n-1}p) = 2x$. Hence x must be a perfect number.

3. The original statement: Let p be an odd prime. If $p \equiv 1 \pmod 4$, then p is the sum of 2 squares.

   The contrapositive statement: Let p be an odd prime. If p is not the sum of 2 squares, then p is not congruent to 1 (mod 4).

   The converse statement: Let p be an odd prime. If p is the sum of 2 squares, then $p \equiv 1 \pmod 4$.

   To prove the converse statement, suppose that p is an odd prime and p is the sum of 2 squares, say $p = a^2 + b^2$. When looking at the numbers mod 4, there are only 4 essentially different numbers: 0, 1, 2, and 3. Squaring these numbers gives us 0, 1, 4, and 9, which are congruent to 0, 1, 0, and 1 (mod 4). Thus if $p = a^2 + b^2$, then p can only equal 0, 1, or 2 (mod 4)—it cannot equal 3 (mod 4). Thus, since p is odd, it must be equal 1 (mod 4).

4. By Fermat's little theorem, since 101 is prime, $2^{101} \equiv 2 \pmod{101}$. Since 2 is relatively prime to 101, we can divide both sides by 2 to get $2^{100} \equiv 1 \pmod{101}$. Alternatively, we can use Euler's theorem. Since 2 is relatively prime to 101, and since 101 is prime, $\phi(101) = 100$, and therefore $2^{100} \equiv 1 \pmod{101}$. Using the power rule, if we raise both sides to the 7th power, we get $2^{700} \equiv 1 \pmod{101}$. Therefore $2^{703} \equiv 2^{700}2^3 \equiv 8 \pmod{101}$.

5. Since $2520 = 2^3 3^2 5^1 7^1$, $\phi(2520) = 2520(1 - 1/2)(1 - 1/3)(1 - 1/5)(1 - 1/7) = 576$. And since 11 is relatively prime to 2520, we know that $11^{576} \equiv 1 \pmod{2520}$. So we multiply by 11, getting $11^{577} \equiv 11 \pmod{2520}$.

Lecture Fifteen

1. Suppose n is composite. Then $n = ab$, where a and b are both bigger than 1. Now suppose to the contrary that n did not contain a divisor (besides 1) that was at most $\sqrt{n}$. Then a and b are both greater than $\sqrt{n}$, and therefore $n = ab > \sqrt{n} \cdot \sqrt{n} = n$, which is a contradiction.

2. Since $493 = 17 \times 29$ (the product of 2 primes), then the only numbers M that are not relatively prime to 493 are those numbers that are multiples of 17 or multiples of 29. There are 29 multiples of 17 below 493 and there are 17 multiples of 29 below 493, and we have counted the number 0 twice. Therefore there are $29 + 17 - 1 = 45$ numbers (between 0 and 493) that are not relatively prime to 493. So the probability of the condition described in the question happening is 45/493.

3. The deciphering number d satisfies the equation $de - \phi(n)f = 1$. Here, $n = 493 = 17 \times 29$, $\phi(n) = 16 \times 28 = 448$, and $e = 303$. We are looking for numbers d and f that satisfy $303d - 448f = 1$. We can find d and f using the Euclidean algorithm: Notice that $448 = 303 + 145$, $303 = 145(2) + 13$, $145 = 13(11) + 2$, and $13 = 2(6) + 1$. Working backward through these equations, we get $1 = 13 - 2(6) = 13 - [145 - 13(11)]6 = 67(13) - 145(6) = 67[303 - 145(2)] - 145(6) = 303(67) - 145(140)$. Therefore, $d = 67$ will be the bank's deciphering number.

4. Here, $p = 71$ and $q = 79$, so $n = pq = 5609$, and $\phi(n) = (p-1)(q-1) = 70 \times 78 = 5460$. We are told that $e = 101$, so we must find d and f so that $101d - 5460f = 1$. Here is another way to find d and f: Let $a = 5460$ and $b = 101$. Subtracting 54 times the second equation from the first gives us $a - 54b = 6$. Now subtract 16 times the third equation from the second to get $-16a + 865b = 5$. Finally, subtract the fourth equation from the third to get $17a - 919b = 1$. Thus $17(5460) - 919(101) = 1$. That is, $101(-919) + 5460(17) = 1$. So $d = -919$ is a solution, or equivalently, $d \equiv -919 \equiv 4541 \pmod{5460}$. So $d = 4541$ will do the trick.

5. For the bank to decipher C^*, it should raise it to the e^* power (mod n^*), which it can do since it knows e^* and n^*. It then raises that to the d power (mod n), which it also knows how to do. The reason this works is that $(C^*)^{e^*} \equiv (C^{d^*})^{e^*} \equiv C^{d^* e^*} \equiv C \pmod{n^*}$. Then $C^e \equiv (M^d)^e = M^{de} \equiv M \pmod{n}$.

Lecture Sixteen

1. **a.** $V = \{1, 2, 3, 4, 5\}$.

    $E = \{\{1, 4\}, \{1, 5\}, \{2, 3\}, \{2, 5\}, \{3, 5\}, \{4, 5\}\}$.

    b. The shortest path from 1 to 3 is 1, 5, 3.

    c. G is Eulerian. It is connected, and every vertex has even degree. An Eulerian tour is 1, 4, 5, 3, 2, 5, 1.

    d. The graph has no Hamiltonian cycle, so it is not Hamiltonian.

2. **a.** Since every pair of vertices is connected by an edge, there are $\binom{n}{2}$ edges.

    b. K_n is connected, and every vertex has degree $n - 1$. Thus every vertex will have even degree if and only if n is odd.

3. Insert a new vertex z adjacent to x and y, creating a new graph, still connected, where every vertex (including x, y, and z) has even degree. Hence the new graph is Eulerian, and we can draw it as an Eulerian cycle that begins at z, takes first step to x, and therefore ends on the edge from y to z. In between the first and last step, we have drawn the original graph G as a trail.

4. The new graph will have exactly 2 vertices of odd degree, x and y, so it can be drawn as a trail that begins at x and ends at y.

5. **a.** The graph can be drawn like this.

    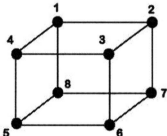

    b. It is not Eulerian because it has 8 vertices of odd degree.

    c. It is Hamiltonian, since it has the Hamiltonian cycle 1, 2, 3, 4, 5, 6, 7, 8, 1.

1. $A = \begin{pmatrix} 0 & 0 & 0 & 1 & 1 \\ 0 & 0 & 1 & 0 & 1 \\ 0 & 1 & 0 & 0 & 1 \\ 1 & 0 & 0 & 0 & 1 \\ 1 & 1 & 1 & 1 & 0 \end{pmatrix}$.

2. By matrix multiplication,

$$A^2 = \begin{pmatrix} 0 & 0 & 0 & 1 & 1 \\ 0 & 0 & 1 & 0 & 1 \\ 0 & 1 & 0 & 0 & 1 \\ 1 & 0 & 0 & 0 & 1 \\ 1 & 1 & 1 & 1 & 0 \end{pmatrix} \begin{pmatrix} 0 & 0 & 0 & 1 & 1 \\ 0 & 0 & 1 & 0 & 1 \\ 0 & 1 & 0 & 0 & 1 \\ 1 & 0 & 0 & 0 & 1 \\ 1 & 1 & 1 & 1 & 0 \end{pmatrix} = \begin{pmatrix} 2 & 1 & 1 & 1 & 1 \\ 1 & 2 & 1 & 1 & 1 \\ 1 & 1 & 2 & 1 & 1 \\ 1 & 1 & 1 & 2 & 1 \\ 1 & 1 & 1 & 1 & 4 \end{pmatrix},$$

   so the number of walks of length 4 from 1 to 5 is the (1, 5) entry of A^4, which is the dot product of (row 1 of A^2) and (column 5 of A^2): $(2\ 1\ 1\ 1\ 1) \cdot (1\ 1\ 1\ 1\ 4) = 2 + 1 + 1 + 1 + 4 = 9$.

3. One way to draw the graph would be this.

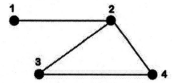

4. **a.** The transition probability matrix looks like this.

$$P = \begin{array}{c} \\ S \\ C \end{array} \begin{array}{cc} S & C \\ \begin{pmatrix} .5 & .5 \\ .25 & .75 \end{pmatrix} \end{array}$$

   b. The (1, 2) entry of P^2 is the dot product of (.5, .5) and (.5, .75) = .25 + .375 = .625.

c. As P is raised to higher and higher powers, it will look like the matrix

$$P* = \begin{array}{cc} & \begin{array}{cc} S & C \end{array} \\ \begin{array}{c} S \\ C \end{array} & \begin{pmatrix} p & 1-p \\ p & 1-p \end{pmatrix} \end{array},$$

which should have the property that it should be unchanged when multiplied by P again. That is, $P*P = P*$, which means that

$$\begin{pmatrix} p & 1-p \\ p & 1-p \end{pmatrix}\begin{pmatrix} .5 & .5 \\ .25 & .75 \end{pmatrix} = \begin{pmatrix} p & 1-p \\ p & 1-p \end{pmatrix}.$$

Equating the (1, 1) entry gives us $.5p + .25(1-p) = p$, which has the solution $p = 1/3$. (Notice that we get the same solution if we equate any entry in the matrix.) Thus, in the long run, 1/3 of the days will be sunny.

1. a.

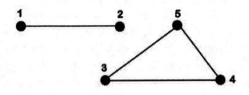

b.

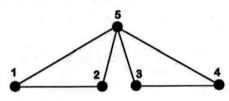

c. Such a graph is impossible since vertex 5 must be adjacent to all 4 other vertices, including vertex 1. But then it would be impossible for $d(1) = 0$.

d. Such a graph is impossible since the sum of the degrees of the vertices is odd.

2. Equivalently, we prove that if the edges of K_{18} are colored red or blue, then it must contain an all-red K_4 or an all-blue K_4. Now consider vertex 18, which must contain at least 9 red edges or at least 9 blue edges, since otherwise it would have at most $8 + 8 = 16 < 17$ edges. Suppose that it has at least 9 red edges, going to vertices 1, 2, ... , 9. Then among these 9 vertices, there must be an all-blue K_4 or an all-red K_3. If it has an all-blue K_4, then we are done. If it has an all-red K_3, using vertices a, b, and c, then along with vertex 18, we have an all-red K_4. The proof when vertex 18 has at least 9 blue edges is similar.

3. Each man can contribute $n!$ possible rankings, and each woman can contribute $n!$ possible rankings, so there are $(n!)^{2n}$ possible lists that the matchmaker can receive.

4. a. In round 1, men 1, 2, 3, 4, and 5 propose to women 3, 1, 5, 1, and 3, respectively. Woman 1 rejects man 2, and woman 3 rejects man 5. Men 2 and 5 then propose to women 3 and 4, respectively, but man 2 is rejected again. Man 2 now proposes to woman 5, who accepts him and rejects man 3. Man 3 proposes to woman 4, who rejects him. Then man 3 proposes to woman 3, who rejects him. Then man 3 proposes to woman 2, who accepts him. With no more unattached men or women, the algorithm terminates with stable pairings: man 1 with woman 3, man 2 with woman 5, man 3 with woman 2, man 4 with woman 1, and man 5 with woman 4.

   b. Here, women 1, 2, 3, 4, and 5 propose to men 3, 3, 1, 5, and 5, respectively, with women 1 and 5 being rejected. Next women 1 and 5 propose to men 5 and 4, respectively, with woman 1 being rejected again. Then woman 1 proposes to man 1, who rejects her. Next woman 1 proposes to man 4, who accepts her and rejects woman 5. Woman 5 proposes to man 4, who accepts her and rejects woman 4. Woman 4 proposes to man 3, who accepts her and rejects woman 2. Woman 2 proposes to man 1, who rejects her. Then woman 2 proposes to man 2, who accepts her. The final stable pairing is man 1 with woman 3, man 2 with woman 2, man 3 with woman 4, man 4 with woman 1, and man 5 with woman 5.

5. a. There are 5 perfect matchings, since once we match vertex 6 to a vertex (5 possible choices), there is exactly 1 way to continue the perfect matching. For example, if we match vertex 6 with vertex 1, then we must match vertex 2 with 3 and vertex 4 with 5.

   b. Applying the logic in part (a) above, if n is even, then W_n has exactly $n - 1$ perfect matchings, but if n is odd, then W_n has no perfect matchings.

Lecture Nineteen

1. **a.** Since every player loses at least 1 match, there is no emperor.

    b. The only Hamiltonian path is 1, 2, 3, 5, 4.

    c. Players 1, 2, and 3 are king chickens.

2. The complete graph K_n has $\binom{n}{2}$ edges, each of which has 2 possible orientations, so the number of tournaments on n vertices is $2^{\binom{n}{2}}$.

3. **a.** The shortest path from 3 to 2 is 3, 1, 2, so $d(3, 2) = 2$.

    b. Suppose that $x \rightarrow y$, then $d(x, y) = 1$ and $d(y, x) > 1$. Otherwise, $d(y, x) = 1$ and $d(y, x) > 1$. Either way, we have $d(x, y) \neq d(y, x)$.

4. With 6 players, there are $\binom{6}{2} = 15$ matches played. It would be impossible for each player to have the same number of victories, since 6 does not divide into 15. In general, in a tournament with $2n$ players, the number of matches played is $\binom{2n}{2} = \dfrac{2n(2n-1)}{2} = n(2n - 1)$, which is not divisible by $2n$, since the fraction $\dfrac{n(2n-1)}{2n} = \dfrac{2n-1}{2}$ is not an integer.

Lecture Twenty

1.

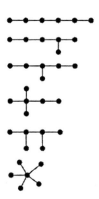

2. The first tree can be labeled $6!/2 = 360$ ways. The second tree can be labeled $6 \times 5 \times 4 \times 3 = 360$ ways by labeling the vertex of degree 3, then its neighbor of degree 2, then the next vertex of degree 2, then the next vertex of degree 1. The third tree can be labeled $(6 \times 5 \times 4!)/2 = 360$ ways by labeling the vertex of degree 3, then its neighbor of degree 1, then the remaining 4 vertices from left to right (dividing by 2 since the same tree results when the labels are reversed). The fourth tree can be labeled $6 \times 5 \times 4 = 120$ ways by labeling the vertex of degree 4, then its neighbor of degree 2, then the next vertex of degree 1. The fifth tree can be labeled $\binom{6}{2}\binom{4}{2} = 90$ ways by deciding the labels for the vertices of degree 3, then for the vertex with the smaller label, choosing its 2 neighbors of degree 1. The sixth graph can be labeled 6 ways by choosing the label of the vertex of degree 5. Altogether, the number of labeled trees is $360 + 360 + 360 + 120 + 90 + 6 = 1296 = 6^4$.

3. Suppose that for every pair of vertices x and y, there exists a unique path from x to y. Then G is necessarily connected. Furthermore, G has no cycles, since if a cycle of length k exists, say, $v_1, v_2, \dots, v_k, v_1$, then there would be more than 1 path from v_1 to v_k. Thus, since G is connected with no cycles, it must be a tree.

4. The minimum weight spanning tree, with total weight 25, is given below.

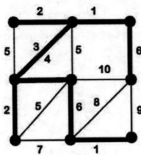

5. For the graph K_4, every vertex has degree 3, so $D = \begin{pmatrix} 3 & 0 & 0 & 0 \\ 0 & 3 & 0 & 0 \\ 0 & 0 & 3 & 0 \\ 0 & 0 & 0 & 3 \end{pmatrix}$

and $A = \begin{pmatrix} 0 & 1 & 1 & 1 \\ 1 & 0 & 1 & 1 \\ 1 & 1 & 0 & 1 \\ 1 & 1 & 1 & 0 \end{pmatrix}$. Therefore, $D - A = \begin{pmatrix} 3 & -1 & -1 & -1 \\ -1 & 3 & -1 & -1 \\ -1 & -1 & 3 & -1 \\ -1 & -1 & -1 & 3 \end{pmatrix}$.

Deleting the last row and column, the determinant of $\begin{pmatrix} 3 & -1 & -1 \\ -1 & 3 & -1 \\ -1 & -1 & 3 \end{pmatrix}$ is $(27 - 1 - 1) - (3 + 3 + 3) = 16$. The answer is not

surprising, since this is the number of labeled trees on 4 vertices, which Cayley's formula tells us is equal to $4^2 = 16$.

Lecture Twenty-One

1. By Euler's planar graph theorem, $n - e + f = 2$, so $9 - 15 + f = 2$; therefore, the graph will have 8 faces.

2. The graph can be redrawn as a plane graph as follows.

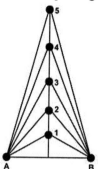

3. According to Euler's planar graph theorem, if the Petersen graph could be drawn as a plane graph, then the number of faces f would equal $2 - n + e = 2 - 10 + 15 = 7$. Thus its edge-face matrix would have 15 rows and 7 columns. Let X be the number of 1s in its edge-face matrix. Then counting row by row, since each edge borders at most 2 faces, we have $X \leq 2e = 30$. On the other hand, counting column by column, since each face (including the external face) uses at least 5 edges, then $X \geq 5f = 35$, which is a contradiction. Hence the Petersen graph is nonplanar.

4. First note that a subdivision of K_5 must contain at least 5 vertices of degree 4. Since the Petersen graph has no vertices of degree 4, it cannot contain a subdivision of K_5. We draw a subdivision of $K_{3,3}$ that is contained in the Petersen graph below. Notice that this graph does not have to use every edge of the Petersen graph.

The Petersen graph

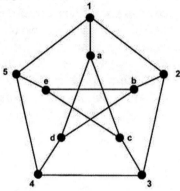

contains

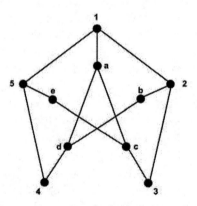

which can be seen to be a subdivision of $K_{3,3}$ by redrawing it as

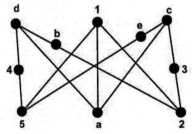

.

Lecture Twenty-Two

1. Since every pair of vertices is connected, any proper coloring of K_n must assign a different color to each vertex; therefore, the chromatic number of K_n is n.

2. Proof by induction. Base case: When $n = 2$, a tree with 2 vertices has chromatic number 2. Inductively assume this is true for any tree with n vertices. Now consider a tree T with $n + 1$ vertices. Removing any leaf and its single edge, we obtain a tree T' with n vertices. By the induction hypothesis, T' has chromatic number 2 and can therefore be properly colored with exactly 2 colors. Returning the leaf to the tree, we can assign the leaf whichever color was not given to its neighbor. Therefore T can be properly colored with 2 colors (not with just 1 color), so it has chromatic number 2.

3. We prove that with m colors at your disposal, you can properly color a tree with n vertices in $m(m - 1)^{n-1}$ ways. When $n = 1$, there are m ways to a color a tree with 1 vertex, and when $n = 2$, there are $m(m - 1)$ ways to color a tree with 2 vertices (m choices for vertex 1 and then $m - 1$ choices for vertex 2). Inductively assume the theorem is true for trees with n vertices, and consider a tree T with $n + 1$ vertices. Removing a leaf from T results in a tree T' with n vertices, which by the induction hypothesis can be properly colored $m(m - 1)^{n-1}$ ways. Returning the leaf to the tree, we can assign the leaf any of the remaining $m - 1$ colors. Therefore, T can be properly colored $m(m - 1)^n$ ways.

4. Suppose, to the contrary, that a planar graph with n vertices had only 1 vertex of degree less than or equal to 5. Then the sum of the degrees of the vertices must be at least $6(n - 1)$. Thus by the handshake theorem, the number of edges is at least $3(n - 1) = 3n - 3$. But this is impossible, since a planar graph has at most $3n - 6$ edges.

5. This is an example of a planar graph where every vertex has degree 5. If every planar graph had to have at least 1 vertex of degree 4 or less, then this could have been used in an inductive proof of the 5-color theorem. (Remove the vertex of degree 4, then properly color the rest of the graph with 5 colors. Bring the degree-4 vertex back, and assign it a color that is different from its 4 neighbors.) A proof of the 4-color theorem could follow by using the Kempe chain argument that was used in the 4-color theorem.

6. We create the graph below, where every vertex represents a course, and 2 vertices x and y are adjacent if a student wants to take course x and course y. The graph can be drawn as follows.

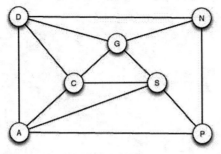

Each time slot is represented by a different color, and a legal assignment corresponds to a proper coloring of the graph, since 2 classes can be offered at the same time only if there is no student who wishes to take both classes. Since the graph is planar, it can be properly colored using 4 colors. (Find a way to do it.) To see that it cannot be done with 3 colors, we observe that vertices C, G, and S must get different colors (since they form a triangle), so we can color them 1, 2, and 3, respectively. But this forces A to get color 2, then D must get color 3, then N must get color 1, but now vertex P is adjacent to vertices with colors 1, 2, and 3, so it must receive a fourth color. Hence we can assign courses C and N in the first time slot, courses A and G in the second time slot, courses D and S in the third time slot, and course P in the fourth time slot.

Lecture Twenty-Three

1. A tree of shortest path is shown in bold below. The shortest path from A to B has length 9 and takes 6 steps.

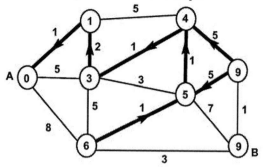

2. Dijkstra's method can be used to determine whether the graph is connected. If a connected graph has n vertices and $n-1$ edges, then it is necessarily a tree. (Why? Because otherwise, the graph would contain a tree with more than $n-1$ edges, which is impossible.) Thus to determine whether the graph is a tree, simply count the edges. If it has $n-1$ edges, then the graph is a tree and contains no cycles. If it has more than $n-1$ edges, then the graph (connected) is not a tree and therefore contains cycles. Note that it is not possible for the graph to have fewer than $n-1$ edges, since it is connected.

3. Problems a, b, c, and e are in the complexity class NP, since if we are given a solution to the problem, it can be verified efficiently. Problem d is not in NP, since it would require checking every subset to answer affirmatively, which cannot be done efficiently. Problem f is not in NP since it is not a decision problem.

Lecture Twenty-Four

1. We have established that a tiling of length $2n - 1$ that uses squares and dominoes must have at least n tiles. How many of these tilings use exactly k squares among their first n tiles? First we choose which k of the first n tiles are assigned to be dominoes. This can be done $\binom{n}{k}$ ways. Since the first n tiles contain k squares (of length 1) and $n - k$ dominoes (of length 2), these first n tiles will have a length of $k + 2(n - k) = 2n - k$. Since the length of the entire strip must be $2n - 1$, we still need to tile the rest of the strip, which has length $(2n - 1) - (2n - k) = k - 1$; this can be tiled in f_{k-1} ways. (Note that when $k = 0$, it is impossible for the first n tiles to be dominoes, since its length would be $2n$, which is too long. But this is accounted for since $f_{-1} = 0$.) Hence, for $0 \leq k \leq n$, the number of tilings of length $2n - 1$ with exactly k squares among its first n tiles is $\binom{n}{k} f_{k-1}$.

   Altogether, the total number of tilings of length $2n - 1$ is $\sum_{k=0}^{n} \binom{n}{k} f_{k-1}$, as desired.

2. You will always end up with the number 9. It is easy to see why if you look at your numbers mod 9. The first number will always have the same digit sum as the second number, so they are equivalent mod 9. In other words, $x \equiv y \pmod 9$, so $x - y \equiv 0 \pmod 9$; therefore, $x - y$ must be a multiple of 9 (but $x - y$ is not 0, since x and y are different numbers). Thus the digits of $x - y$ must sum to a multiple of 9.

3. The domino trick would not have worked with values 0 through 9, since its underlying graph would be K_{10}. The success of the domino trick with values 0 through 6 depended on the fact that its underlying graph, K_7, is Eulerian, since every vertex has even degree (6). But in the graph K_{10}, every vertex has odd degree (9), and K_{10} is not Eulerian. In fact, if we remove a single domino, then the resulting graph will have 8 vertices of odd degree (and 2 vertices of even degree), so it will not even be possible to create a chain of dominoes in the first place. But the trick would work if you secretly removed 4 dominoes with all different values—say, $\{0, 1\}$, $\{2, 3\}$, $\{4, 5\}$, and $\{6, 7\}$—since now there would be exactly 2 vertices of odd degree, vertices 8 and 9, which would have to be the endpoints of the chain.

4. You will end up on card 3 thanks to parity. When starting at card 1 (ace) or 5, you begin by taking an odd number of steps, which forces you to land on an even card, card 2 or card 4, so cards 1 (ace) and 5 can be safely removed. Next you take an odd number of steps, which forces you to land on the only odd-valued card, card 3.

Timeline

1736 ....Leonhard Euler (1707–1783) lays the foundations of graph theory by solving the bridges of Königsberg problem. That same year, he generalizes Fermat's little theorem using the phi function $\phi(m)$. (He discovered his planar graph formula, $n - e + f = 2$, around 1750.)

1801 ....Carl Friedrich Gauss (1777–1855) publishes his book *Disquisitiones Arithmeticae*. This important book contains the first treatment of modular arithmetic.

1852 ....The 4-color map problem is introduced to the mathematics community.

1876 ....Édouard Lucas (1842–1891) proves that $2^{127} - 1$ is prime, which remained the largest known prime number until 1951.

1915 ....Influential combinatorics textbook by Percy Alexander MacMahon appears, *Combinatory Analysis*.

1938 ....Hardy and Wright publish their landmark *Introduction to the Theory of Numbers*.

1951 ....J. C. P. Miller and D. J. Wheeler begin use of a computer to find much larger primes, including $(180)(2^{127} - 1)^2 + 1$.

1957 ....*Introduction to Finite Mathematics* by John Kemeny, James Snell, and Gerald Thompson is the first mainstream textbook to survey discrete mathematics.

1958 ....The first major textbook on graph theory appears, in French; translated into English in 1962.

1969 ....The concept of the Erdös number is invented, named after prolific mathematician Paul Erdös.

1971 ....The journal *Discrete Mathematics* begins publication.

1971 ....Stephen Cook proves that the satisfiability problem is NP-complete.

1977 ....The most famous method for public key cryptography, the RSA method, is discovered by 3 mathematically trained computer scientists, Ronald Rivest, Adi Shamier, and Leonard Adleman.

1977 ....The 4-color theorem is proved by Wolfgang Haken and Kenneth Appel.

1995 ....Andrew Wiles proves Fermat's last theorem.

2002 ....A polynomial time algorithm is discovered to determine if a number is prime.

2008 ....The number $2^{43,112,609} - 1$ becomes the largest prime number yet discovered.

Glossary

adjacency matrix: A matrix with (i, j) entry equal to the number of edges that connect vertex i to vertex j in a given graph.

algorithm: A method for solving a problem in a finite number of steps.

arrangement: A listing of objects where order matters, but repetition is not allowed.

Bézout's theorem (a.k.a. Bézout's identity): The greatest common divisor of a and b is the smallest positive number of the form $ax + by$, where x and y are integers. Named in honor of a more general result by Étienne Bézout (1730–1783).

Binet's formula: A closed form for the Fibonacci numbers. For

$$n \geq 0, \ F_n = \frac{1}{\sqrt{5}} \left[\left(\frac{1+\sqrt{5}}{2} \right)^n - \left(\frac{1-\sqrt{5}}{2} \right)^n \right].$$

binomial coefficient: $\binom{n}{k}$, pronounced "n choose k"; the number of size-k subsets of $\{1, 2, \ldots, n\}$, or equivalently, the number of ways to choose k objects from n, where order is not important and repetition is not allowed.

binomial theorem: It states that for any real or complex numbers x and y and any non-negative integer n,

$$(x + y)^n = \sum_{k=0}^{n} \binom{n}{k} x^k y^{n-k}.$$

cancellation theorem: If $ax \equiv ay \pmod{m}$ and if $\gcd(a, m) = 1$, then $x \equiv y \pmod{m}$.

Carmichael number: A composite number that passes the Fermat primality test for every base. In 1994, 3 mathematicians proved that there must be an infinite number of Carmichael numbers. Named for American mathematician Robert Carmichael (1879–1967).

Cayley's formula: For $n \geq 1$, the number of trees with n vertices is n^{n-2}. Stated in 1854 without graph theory in a result by Arthur Cayley (1821–1895).

Chinese remainder theorem: If m_1 and m_2 are relatively prime, then there is a solution to the system of congruences $x \equiv a \pmod{m_1}$ and $x \equiv b \pmod{m_2}$. The solution is unique $(\bmod\ m_1 m_2)$. Originated in China during the 3rd century C.E. but first published as a theorem by a Chinese government official in 1247.

chromatic number: The chromatic number of a graph G is the smallest number k for which G has a proper coloring that uses k different colors.

combinatorial proof: Showing that an equation is true by showing that the left side and right side of the equation are both solutions to the same counting question.

combinatorics: The mathematics of counting.

complete graph: A graph is complete if every pair of vertices is adjacent. The complete graph on n vertices is denoted by K_n.

complexity: The complexity of an algorithm is the number of steps to solve a problem of a given size. If a problem has size n, and the number of steps is bounded by a polynomial function of n, then the algorithm is considered to be efficient. If a decision problem has an efficient algorithm, then that problem belongs in the complexity class P.

composite: A positive number with 3 or more positive divisors.

congruence: We say $a \equiv b \pmod{m}$ ("a is congruent to b mod m") if m divides $a - b$; equivalently, a and b have the same remainder when divided by m.

contradiction, proof by: A proof technique that begins by assuming that the theorem is false, then showing how that leads to an impossible conclusion.

contrapositive: The contrapositive of the statement "If p, then q" is the statement "If not q, then not p." It is logically equivalent to the original statement.

converse: The converse of the statement "If p, then q" is the statement "If q, then p." It is not equivalent to the original statement.

cycle: A closed trail with no repeated vertices, except for the endpoints.

De Bruijn sequence: A sequence of binary code words where all 2^n binary code words of length n can be encapsulated in a single list of 2^n numbers. Named for Dutch mathematician Nicolaas Govert de Bruijn, whose work on such sequences appeared in 1946.

degree: The degree of a vertex v, denoted $d(v)$, is the number of vertices adjacent to v.

Dijkstra's algorithm: An efficient algorithm for finding the shortest path between any pair of vertices in a weighted graph. Introduced in 1959 by Dutch computer scientist Edsger Dijkstra (1930–2002).

division theorem: For positive integers a and d, there are unique integers q and r such that $a = dq + r$, where $0 \leq r < d$.

drawable: A graph G is drawable if it is connected and there exists a trail that uses every edge of G.

Euclid's algorithm: For any numbers a, b, x, $\gcd(a, b) = \gcd(b, a - bx)$. More specifically, $\gcd(a, b) = \gcd(b, a \bmod b)$.

Eulerian graph: A graph G is Eulerian if it is connected and there exists a closed trail that uses every edge of G.

Eulerian graph theorem: A graph is Eulerian if and only if it is connected and every vertex has an even degree.

Euler's planar graph theorem: For any connected planar graph with n vertices, e edges, and f faces, $n - e + f = 2$.

Euler's theorem (number theory): If $\gcd(a, m) = 1$, then $a^{\phi(m)} \equiv 1 \pmod{m}$.

factorial: $n!$ is the product $n(n - 1)(n - 2) \cdots (1)$. It counts the number of ways to arrange n distinct objects. For example, $4! = 4 \times 3 \times 2 \times 1 = 24$. The number $0!$ is defined to be 1.

Fermat primality test: If there exists an integer a such that a^n is not congruent to $a \pmod{n}$, then n is not prime.

Fermat's last theorem: For $n > 2$, there do not exist positive integers x, y, and z such that $x^n + y^n = z^n$.

Fermat's little theorem: For prime p and any integer a, $a^p \equiv a \pmod{p}$.

Fibonacci numbers: The numbers 0, 1, 1, 2, 3, 5, 8, 13, 21, 34, 55, 89, 144, … ; they are defined by $F_0 = 0$, $F_1 = 1$, and for $n \geq 2$, $F_n = F_{n-1} + F_{n-2}$. They were first introduced by Leonardo of Pisa in his book *Liber Abaci*.

forest: An unconnected graph with no cycles.

4-color theorem: A map of the counties of any state can always be colored in such a way that no adjacent counties are assigned the same color, and we need at most 4 colors to achieve this.

fundamental theorem of arithmetic: Also known as the unique factorization theorem; states that every positive number has a unique factorization into prime numbers.

Gaussian integer: A complex number of the form $a + bi$, where a and b are integers and i is an imaginary number whose square is -1.

Gaussian prime: A Gaussian integer that cannot be factored into Gaussian integers xy unless x or y is 1, -1, i, or $-i$.

geometric proof: Proving a theorem by drawing a picture, often by decomposing a diagram in 2 different ways.

graph: A finite set of vertices, where some pairs $\binom{n}{n}$ of vertices are connected by an edge.

graph theory: The study of graphs—mathematical structures used to model pairwise relations between objects from a certain collection.

greatest common divisor: The largest positive integer that divides 2 numbers without remainder.

Hamiltonian graph: A graph that contains a cycle going through every vertex.

Hamiltonian path: A path that goes through every vertex of a given graph.

handshake theorem: The sum of the degrees of the vertices of a graph must be twice the number of edges.

important theorem: If d divides ab, and d is relatively prime to a, then d divides b.

induction: A proof technique for proving theorems by showing that if the theorem is true for the number k, then it will continue to be true for the number $k + 1$.

induction hypothesis (IHOP): The assumption in the inductive step (*see* **induction**) that the statement holds for some n.

inshuffle: A perfect shuffle where the top and bottom card do not stay at the top and bottom.

integer combination theorem: If $d|a$ and $d|b$, then $d|(ax + by)$ for any integers x and y.

king chicken theorem: In a tournament, x is a king chicken, or simply a king, if for every opponent y, either x beats y or there exists a player z such that x beat z and z beat y. In other words, a king is a player that can walk to any vertex in at most 2 steps.

Kuratowski's theorem: Every nonplanar graph contains inside it nonplanar graph K_5 or $K_{3,3}$ or a subdivision of K_5 or $K_{3,3}$ Proved by Polish mathematician Kazimierz Kuratowski in 1930. The capital K for the graphs K_n and $K_{m,n}$ is used in his honor.

least common multiple: The smallest positive number that is a multiple of 2 numbers.

Lucas numbers: An integer sequence named after the mathematician François Édouard Anatole Lucas. Like the Fibonacci numbers, each Lucas number is defined to be the sum of its 2 immediate previous terms. However, the first 2 Lucas numbers are 2 and 1 instead of 0 and 1. The sequence of Lucas numbers begins 2, 1, 3, 4, 7, 11, 18, 29, 47, 76, 123, … .

Markov chain: A random walk on a graph, where the probability of moving from vertex i to vertex j is given by a fixed probability p_{ij}.

matrix: A box of numbers.

minimum spanning tree: A tree that connects all the vertices of a weighted graph in such a way as to minimize the sum of the weights of the edges.

modulus: When doing modular arithmetic, you are interested in the remainders when dividing by a particular number m. The number m is called the modulus. The number x mod m is the remainder obtained when dividing x by m. In congruence statements, $x \equiv y \pmod{m}$ means that x and y have the same remainder when divided by m.

multichoose: The number $\left(\!\!\binom{n}{k}\!\!\right)$, pronounced "$n$ multichoose k," is the number of size-k multisubsets of $\{1, 2, \ldots, n\}$, or equivalently, the number of ways to choose k objects from n, where order is not important, but repetition is allowed.

multigraph: A graph that allows some pairs of vertices to be connected by more than 1 edge.

multinomial coefficient: The number $n!/(a!b!c!)$, where $a + b + c = n$, counts the ways to allocate n distinct pieces of candy so that child 1 gets a pieces, child 2 gets b pieces, and child 3 gets c pieces.

multiplicative inverse: Among the real numbers, the multiplicative inverse of the number b is the number $1/b$, since when we multiply them together we get the number 1. In modular arithmetic, when working with modulus m, the multiplicative inverse is a number c for which $bc \equiv 1 \pmod{m}$. With modulus m, b has a multiplicative inverse if and only if b is relatively prime to m.

multiset: A collection of objects where order does not matter, but repetition is allowed.

multisubset: The multiset X is a multisubset of the set Y if every element of X belongs to Y.

NP (nondeterministic polynomial): The set of decision problems where a yes answer can be verified in polynomial time.

number theory: The study of the natural numbers 0, 1, 2, 3, … .

outshuffle: A perfect shuffle where the top card stays on top and the bottom card stays on the bottom.

parity principle: A way of figuring out many mathematical conundrums by simply keeping track of odd numbers and even numbers.

partition number: $p_k(n)$ is the number of ways that the number n can be expressed as the sum of k positive integers, where order is not important. For example, $p_3(5) = 2$, since $5 = 3 + 1 + 1$ and $5 = 2 + 2 + 1$. The number $p(n)$ is the number of ways that n can be expressed as the sum of (any number of) positive integers, where order is not important. For example, $p(4) = 4$, since $4 = 3 + 1 = 2 + 2 = 2 + 1 + 1 = 1 + 1 + 1 + 1$.

Pascal's triangle: A triangle where, for $n \geq 0$, the elements of row n are the binomial coefficients $\binom{n}{0}, \binom{n}{1}, \binom{n}{2}, \ldots, \binom{n}{n}$.

path: A walk with no repeated vertices.

perfect shuffle: A shuffle where the deck is cut exactly in half, and the cards from each half are interlaced together perfectly. There are 2 types of perfect shuffles, inshuffles and outshuffles.

permutation: An arrangement of distinct objects; sometimes defined as the number of ways that k objects can be chosen from n objects, where order is important and repetition is allowed, and counted by the formula $n!/(n-k)!$. When $k = n$, the number of permutations is $n!$, pronounced "n factorial."

pigeonhole principle: If $n + 1$ objects are placed into n containers, then there must exist a container with at least 2 objects.

planar graph: A graph that can be drawn on a sheet of paper in such a way that none of its edges cross.

power theorem: If $a \equiv b \pmod{m}$, then $an \equiv bn \pmod{m}$ for any exponent $n \geq 0$.

prime: A positive number with exactly 2 divisors, 1 and itself.

prime important theorem: If prime p divides ab, then p divides a or p divides b. More generally, if prime p divides the product of n numbers, then p divides at least 1 of the numbers.

principle of inclusion-exclusion (PIE): A method for solving certain combinatorics problems that is as easy as PIE!

problem of points: A gambling problem, discovered by Blaise Pascal, which seeks to determine the appropriate settlement amount between 2 players, with a score of x to y, where the first person to reach n points wins d dollars.

proper coloring: The vertices of a graph G are properly colored if every vertex is assigned a color in such a way that no adjacent vertices have the same color. A similar definition applies to properly coloring the edges of a graph or the faces of a planar graph.

Ramsey number: The Ramsey number $R(a, b)$ is the smallest value of n for which a coloring of the complete graph K_n using red and blue edges must result in an all-red K_a or an all-blue K_b. For example, $R(3, 3) = 6$.

Ramsey's theorem: For any positive numbers a and b, there is a number n such that if all edges of the complete graph K_n are colored red or blue, then there must exist an all-red K_a or an all-blue K_b.

relatively prime: Two numbers are relatively prime if their greatest common divisor is 1.

RSA method: An easily implemented method for public key cryptography. Published in 1977 by MIT computer scientists Ronald Rivest, Adi Shamir, and Leonard Adleman.

rule of product: The idea that if we have a ways of doing something and b ways of doing another thing, then there are ab ways of performing both actions.

rule of sum: The idea that if we have a ways of doing something and b ways of doing another thing and we cannot do both at the same time, then there are $a + b$ ways to choose one of the actions.

sequence: A listing of objects, where order matters and repetition is allowed.

set: A collection of distinct objects, where order does not matter.

skip sum identity: $\sum_{k=0}^{n} \binom{n}{k} (-1)^k = 0$.

stable marriage problem: Given a collection of n eligible men and women, find a pairing of them so that no extramarital affairs will take place.

Stirling number: $S(n, m)$ denotes the number of ways of partitioning a set of n distinct elements into m nonempty subsets. These are also called Stirling numbers of the second kind. Stirling numbers of the first kind, also sometimes denoted by $S(n, m)$, denote the number of permutations of n elements that have exactly m cycles, or equivalently, the number of ways n people can sit around m identical circular tables so that no tables are unoccupied. Introduced by James Stirling (1692–1770).

subset: The set X is a subset of the set Y if every element of X belongs to Y.

tournament: A complete graph where every edge has an orientation. An edge that points from i to j can be thought of as player i defeating player j in a tournament where everyone plays everyone else in 1 game.

trail: A walk with no repeated edges. If the first and last vertex are the same, then the trail is closed.

traveling salesman problem: Find a Hamiltonian cycle in a weighted graph whose total weight is minimized.

tree: A connected graph with no cycles.

tribonacci numbers: A member of an integer sequence defined similarly to the Fibonacci numbers, except that each term equals the sum of the previous 3 terms in the series. The first few terms are 1, 1, 2, 4, 7, 13, 24, 44, and 81.

walk: A sequence of adjacent vertices where repetition is allowed.

weighted graph: A graph whose edges are assigned weights. The weight could reflect the cost of using the edge.

Wilson's theorem: Stated by John Wilson and proven by Joseph-Louis Lagrange in 1771: n is prime if and only if $(n - 1)! \equiv -1 \pmod{n}$.

Biographical Notes

Binet, Jacques (1786–1856): French mathematician who worked in number theory and matrix theory. The closed form expression for the Fibonacci numbers is named after him.

Erdös, Paul (1913–1996): Hungarian-born mathematician, second only to Euler in all-time output, who authored or coauthored approximately 1500 papers. Choosing to have no formal professional position, he traveled from institution to institution to work with colleagues in number theory, probability, set theory, combinatorics, and graph theory. The notion of the Erdös number gave humorous recognition to his wide-ranging influence across 20th-century mathematics.

Euler, Leonhard (1707–1783): Swiss mathematician and scientist who worked in St. Petersburg and Berlin and was probably the most productive and influential mathematician of all time, introducing many ideas and notations still in use. He laid the foundations of graph theory by solving the bridges of Königsberg problem in 1736. That same year, he generalized Fermat's little theorem using $\phi(m)$, which later came to be called the totient function. He discovered his planar graph formula, $n - e + f = 2$, around 1750. He was father to 13 children, and he produced nearly half of his enormous mathematical output after losing nearly all his sight in 1771.

Fermat, Pierre de (1601–1655): French lawyer in Toulouse who was a leading contributor to number theory and analytic geometry. He discovered what is now called his little theorem (that any prime number p divides $a^p - a$) in 1640. His so-called last theorem famously appeared as a note in the margin of his copy of Diophantus's *Arithmetica*.

Fibonacci (a.k.a. **Leonardo of Pisa**; c. 1170–c. 1240): Italian mathematician from Pisa whose book *Liber Abaci* (1202) introduced what in the 19th century came to be called Fibonacci numbers as part of an arithmetical exercise that involved the counting of pairs of rabbits. Thanks to extensive travel in his youth, he learned the Hindu-Arabic numeral system, which he introduced to Europe in several important books.

Gauss, Carl Friedrich (1777–1855): Preeminent German mathematician and astronomer who spent most of his career at Göttingen and whose contributions span geometry, number theory, and analysis. He established mathematical rigor as the standard of proof, and his important *Disquisitiones Arithmeticae* (1801) contained the first treatment of modular arithmetic. Gauss's biographer quoted him as having said, "Mathematics is the queen of the sciences, and number theory is the queen of mathematics," while Gauss himself is often known as the Prince of Mathematics.

Hamilton, William Rowan (1805–1865): Irish mathematician whose invention of the algebra of quaternions later played a role in the development of quantum mechanics. Late in his career, his study of closed paths going exactly once through each vertex of a dodecahedron formed the basis of what became known as Hamiltonian graphs—an idea that he also turned into a board game (the Icosian Game).

Hardy, G. H. (1887–1947): English mathematician whose preference for pure mathematics was evident as early as the first edition of his influential textbook, *A Course of Pure Mathematics* (1908). Hardy arranged for Srinivasa Ramanujan to study and collaborate at the University of Cambridge during 1914–1919. Despite Hardy's disdain for applied mathematics—he once said, "No discovery of mine has made, or is likely to make directly, or indirectly, for good or ill, the least difference to anyone in the world"—he independently discovered a cornerstone of population genetics, later known as the Hardy-Weinberg law (1908). His cowritten *Introduction to the Theory of Numbers* (1938) remains in print today and was the considered the standard reference on the subject for much of the 20th century.

Lucas, Édouard (1842–1891): French mathematician who worked in various areas of number theory. He discovered many interesting properties of the Fibonacci numbers, which he named after Fibonacci, and he also investigated a related sequence that we now call Lucas numbers. In 1876, he proved that $2^{127} - 1$ is prime, using methods for prime number testing that are still used today.

Markov, Andrey (1856–1922): Russian mathematician who followed early work in number theory with important results in the probability of related events, in which events are both random yet also linked to one another in what are now known as Markov chains.

Pascal, Blaise (1623–1662): French mathematician who discovered what came to be known as Pascal's triangle in 1654 when analyzing a problem that arose from gambling, called the problem of points. Pascal became the first mathematician to explore the triangle's many properties in his treatise *Traité du Triangle Arithmétique* (1655).

Ramanujan, Srinivasa (1887–1920): Largely self-taught Indian mathematician who is considered one of the mathematical geniuses of the 20th century, best known for his contributions to number theory and analysis. His work on integer partitions continues to intrigue and inspire number theorists and combinatorialists today.

Ramsey, Frank P. (1903–1930): British mathematician, economist, and philosopher whose combinatorial theorem regarding the coloring of graphs (e.g., the number of friends and strangers in a given group) led to efforts to identify what are now called Ramsey numbers and to so-called Ramsey theory, which studies the emergence of order as numbers become extremely large.

Bibliography

Benjamin, Arthur T., and Ezra Brown, eds. *Biscuits of Number Theory*. Vol. 34 of *Dolciani Mathematical Expositions*. Washington, DC: Mathematical Association of America, 2009. A collection of 40 exceptionally well-written articles; suitable for anyone taking a first course in number theory.

Benjamin, Arthur T., and Jennifer J. Quinn. *Proofs That Really Count: The Art of Combinatorial Proof*. Vol. 27 of *Dolciani Mathematical Expositions*. Washington, DC: Mathematical Association of America, 2003. More than 200 identities, many using Fibonacci numbers, Lucas numbers, and binomial coefficients, are given elementary combinatorial proofs.

Bogart, Kenneth P. *Introductory Combinatorics*. 2nd ed. New York: Harcourt Brace Jovanovich, 1990. A well-written, comprehensive intermediate-level combinatorics textbook.

Chartrand, Gary. *Introductory Graph Theory*. New York: Dover Publications, 1977. An excellent (and inexpensive!) introduction to graph theory, filled with many applications.

Dudley, Underwood. *Elementary Number Theory*. 2nd ed. New York: Dover Publications, 1978. An excellent (and inexpensive!) introduction to number theory, written with clarity and wit.

Edwards, A. W. F. *Pascal's Arithmetical Triangle: The Story of a Mathematical Idea*. Baltimore, MD: Johns Hopkins University Press, 2002. An accurate account of the origins of Pascal's triangle and some of its earliest applications.

Garey, Michael R., and David S. Johnson. *Computers and Intractability: A Guide to the Theory of NP-Completeness*. New York: W. H. Freeman, 1979. The standard reference on the theory of NP-completeness.

Graham, Ronald L., Donald E. Knuth, and Oren Patashnik. *Concrete Mathematics: A Foundation for Computer Science*. 2nd ed. Reading, MA: Addison Wesley, 1994. This is an intermediate-level discrete mathematics book that is suitable for someone who has completed this course. It combines CONtinuous math with disCRETE math, while devoting considerable attention to the evaluation of sums that arise in many combinatorial problems. Most pages are sprinkled with graffiti submitted by the authors and their students, providing additional insights and humor.

Gross, Benedict, and Joe Harris. *The Magic of Numbers*. Upper Saddle River, NJ: Pearson Prentice Hall, 2004. One of the best introductions to rigorous mathematical thinking. This is not so much a textbook to be studied as a book to be read and enjoyed.

Hardy, G. H., and E. M. Wright. *An Introduction to the Theory of Numbers*. 5th ed. Oxford: Oxford University Press, 1978. Originally published in 1938, this classic of number theory was actually updated 40 years later by the second author. Although not the most elementary introduction to the subject, since some of the material requires calculus, it was the standard reference on the subject for decades.

Hopkins, Brian, and Robin Wilson. "The Truth about Königsberg." *The College Mathematics Journal* 35 (2004): 198–207. A well-written article about what Euler proved and did not prove about the bridges of Königsberg.

Lovász, L., J. Pelikán, and K. Vesztergombi. *Discrete Mathematics: Elementary and Beyond*. New York: Springer-Verlag, 2003. This is probably the book that comes closest to capturing this *Discrete Mathematics* course, and I sometimes use it as a required textbook for my discrete math course at Harvey Mudd College.

Maurer, Stephen B. "The King Chicken Theorems." *Mathematics Magazine* 53 (1980): 67–80. A flock of results about pecking orders, describing possible patterns of dominance. (This article is viewable online at the website of the Mathematical Association of America, www.maa.org.)

Morris, S. Brent. *Magic Tricks, Card Shuffling, and Dynamic Computer Memories*. Washington, DC: Mathematical Association of America, 1998. Everything you ever wanted to know about the mathematics of perfect shuffles—and some magic tricks that can be performed once you have mastered the skill.

Niven, Ivan, Herbert S. Zuckerman, and Hugh L. Montgomery. *An Introduction to the Theory of Numbers*. 5th ed. New York: John Wiley and Sons, 1991. An intermediate-level textbook on number theory.

Rosen, Kenneth H. *Discrete Mathematics and Its Applications*. 5th ed. New York: McGraw-Hill, 2003. Probably the bestselling textbook on discrete mathematics, adopted at many colleges and universities.

Scheinerman, Edward. *Mathematics: A Discrete Introduction*. 2nd ed. Belmont, CA: Thomson Brooks/Cole, 2006. A terrific introduction to abstract reasoning and mathematical proof writing by way of discrete mathematical topics.

Silverman, Joseph H. *A Friendly Introduction to Number Theory*. Upper Saddle River, NJ: Prentice Hall, 1997. Like the title says, an extremely accessible introduction to the theory of numbers.

Stanley, Richard P. *Enumerative Combinatorics*. Vol. 1. Cambridge: Cambridge University Press, 1997. A graduate-level course in combinatorics.

Tucker, Alan. *Applied Combinatorics*. 4th ed. New York: John Wiley and Sons, 2002. A very readable textbook on combinatorics and graph theory, loaded with fun and interesting problems.

West, Douglas B. *Introduction to Graph Theory*. 2nd ed. Upper Saddle River, NJ: Prentice Hall, 2001. An intermediate-level textbook on graph theory.

Wilf, Herbert S. *Algorithms and Complexity*. 2nd ed. Natick, MA: AK Peters, 2002. An intermediate-level textbook on the analysis of algorithms and computational complexity.

Wilson, Robin. *Four Colors Suffice: How the Map Problem Was Solved*. Princeton, NJ: Princeton University Press, 2002. A very readable account of the history and solution of the 4-color theorem.

Young, Robert M. *Excursions in Calculus: An Interplay of the Continuous and the Discrete*. Vol. 13 of *Dolciani Mathematical Expositions*. Washington, DC: Mathematical Association of America, 1992. Despite its title, it is really a book on number theory for people who have studied discrete mathematics and some calculus. The exposition is first-rate.

Notes

Notes